S207 The Physical World
Science: Level 2

The Open

The restless Universe

Edited by Robert Lambourne and John Bolton

S207 Course Team

Course Team Chair	Robert Lambourne
Academic Editors	John Bolton, Alan Durrant, Robert Lambourne, Joy Manners, Andy Norton
Authors	David Broadhurst, Derek Capper, Dan Dubin, Tony Evans, Ian Halliday, Carole Haswell, Keith Higgins, Keith Hodgkinson, Mark Jones, Sally Jordan, Ray Mackintosh, David Martin, John Perring, Michael de Podesta, Ian Saunders, Richard Skelding, Tony Sudbery, Stan Zochowski
Consultants	Alan Cayless, Melvin Davies, Graham Farmelo, Stuart Freake, Gloria Medina, Kerry Parker, Alice Peasgood, Graham Read, Russell Stannard, Chris Wigglesworth
Course Managers	Gillian Knight, Michael Watkins
Course Secretaries	Tracey Moore, Tracey Woodcraft
BBC	Deborah Cohen, Tessa Coombs, Steve Evanson, Lisa Hinton, Michael Peet, Jane Roberts
Editors	Gerry Bearman, Rebecca Graham, Ian Nuttall, Peter Twomey
Graphic Designers	Steve Best, Sue Dobson, Sarah Hofton, Pam Owen
Centre for Educational Software staff	Geoff Austin, Andrew Bertie, Canan Blake, Jane Bromley, Philip Butcher, Chris Denham, Nicky Heath, Will Rawes, Jon Rosewell, Andy Sutton, Fiona Thomson, Rufus Wondre
Course Assessor	Roger Blin-Stoyle
Picture Researcher	Lydia K. Eaton

The Course Team wishes to thank Mark Jones for his contribution to the multimedia package 'Space and the Universe'. Grateful acknowledgement is made to John A Ey III/ Science Photo Library for the use of the image on the cover.

The Open University, Walton Hall, Milton Keynes MK7 6AA

First published 2000

Copyright © 2007 The Open University

Written, edited, designed and typeset by the Open University.

Printed and bound in the United Kingdom by Latimer Trend & Company Ltd, Plymouth.

ISBN 978 0 7492 1912 3

This text forms part of an Open University course, S207 *The Physical World*. Details of this and other Open University courses can be obtained from the Course Reservations Centre, PO Box 724, The Open University, Milton Keynes MK7 6ZS, United Kingdom: tel. +44 (0) 1908 653231; e-mail ces-gen@open.ac.uk

Alternatively, you may visit the Open University website at http://www.open.ac.uk where you can learn more about the wide range of courses and packs offered at all levels by the Open University.

To purchase this publication or other components of Open University courses, contact Open University Worldwide Ltd, The Berrill Building, Walton Hall, Milton Keynes MK7 6AA, United Kingdom: tel. +44 (0) 1908 858785, fax +44 (0) 1908 858787, e-mail ouwenq@open.ac.uk; website http://www.ouw.co.uk

2.1

s207book1i2.1

FSC
Mixed Sources
Product group from well-managed forests and other controlled sources
Cert no. SGS-COC-005493
www.fsc.org
© 1996 Forest Stewardship Council

The paper used in this publication contains pulp sourced from forests independently certified to the Forest Stewardship Council (FSC) principles and criteria. Chain of custody certification allows the pulp from these forests to be tracked to the end use (see www.fsc.org).

BOOK 1: THE RESTLESS UNIVERSE

Course preface: *The Physical World*

Welcome to *The Physical World*. This book is the first in a series of eight that provide an introduction to the main ideas and applications of physics. The books have been planned, designed and edited by staff at the Open University, the United Kingdom's largest university and one of the world's major distance teaching institutions. The books are intended for self-study and therefore provide a greater degree of support than most other textbooks.

The titles of the eight books are:

1   The restless Universe
2   Describing motion
3   Predicting motion
4   Classical physics of matter

5   Static fields and potentials
6   Dynamic fields and waves
7   Quantum physics: an introduction
8   Quantum physics of matter

The Open University course S207 *The Physical World* includes a variety of learning materials apart from the texts, most notably multimedia and videos. Each of these media has an important role to play in the overall strategy of the course. They are *essential* for Open University students and will be referred to at various points in the text. However if you are not studying with the Open University, and do not have access to these additional media, the books can be read in isolation: they provide a coherent introduction to physics, independent of other resources.

The production of *The Physical World* was made possible by generous contributions of time and effort from many individuals at a variety of institutions. We gratefully acknowledge these contributions and thank all the contributors, some of whom are named in the list inside the front cover. All those who have been involved with the production of *The Physical World* hope that it will deepen your understanding of our remarkable Universe and its laws. We also hope that you will enjoy learning about physics, its applications and its cultural significance.

John Bolton   Alan Durrant   Robert Lambourne   Joy Manners   Andrew Norton

Academic Editors of *The Physical World*

Introduction to Book 1

Studying physics will change you as a person. At least it should. In studying physics you will encounter some of the deepest and most far-reaching concepts that have ever entered human consciousness. Knowledge gathered over many centuries, that has been subjected to continuous scientific scrutiny, will be presented, along with its applications. Fact will follow fact, useful theory will succeed useful theory. Amidst this rich mix of information, newcomers to physics might not always appreciate how major discoveries have radically changed our attitude to ourselves, our natural environment, and our place in the Universe. In *The Physical World* we have tried to avoid intellectual overload, to ensure that you have sufficient time to appreciate the significance of each of the main ideas and applications of physics. We want your exposure to physics to change you, and we want you to be consciously aware of that change.

As part of that effort, this book gives a qualitative overview of some of the 'big ideas' of physics. Presenting ideas in this way, largely shorn of detail, and without much of the evidence that supports them, should help you to see the big picture and to appreciate some of the deep links that exist between different parts of physics. But this approach also has its dangers. It may obscure the fact that physics is more than a set of ideas about the world, more than a bunch of results: physics is also a *process*, a way of investigating the world based on experiment and observation. One of the biggest of all the 'big ideas' is that claims about the physical world must ultimately be tested by experiment and observation. Maintaining contact with the real world in this way is the guiding principle behind all scientific investigations, including those carried out by physicists.

Another important function of this book is to stress that physics is a cultural enterprise. All too often physics can have the appearance of being a collection of facts, theories, laws and techniques that have somehow emerged from nowhere. This, of course, is not the case. Throughout the ages, it has been the endeavour of individual men and women that has made possible the growth of science and the advancement of physics. This book attempts to emphasize the cultural aspect of physics by providing biographical information about some great physicists of the past. The coverage is neither fair nor complete, but it should remind you that physics is a human creation. Most physicists delight in tales of the struggles, foibles and achievements of their predecessors, and many feel that their understanding of physics is enhanced by knowing something of the paths (including the dead ends) that their intellectual forbears have trodden.

Do not expect to understand everything you read in this book. On the surface, we hope that it provides a coherent and interesting survey. But the more you think about some of the issues raised, the more puzzling they may seem. If, at the end of the book, you are left with questions as well as answers, that will be an excellent starting point for the rest of the course.

> You should leave the text at this point and use the multimedia package *Space and the Universe*. At the end of this activity you should return to this text.

A note on powers of ten and significant figures

Physics involves many quantities that may be very large or very small. When discussing such quantities it is convenient to use *powers of ten notation*. According to this notation

$$1\,000\,000 = 10^6 = \text{a million}$$

$$\frac{1}{1000} = 0.001 = 10^{-3} = \text{a thousandth.}$$

The small superscript attached to the ten is called a *power*. As illustrated by the above examples, a positive power indicates the number of zeros after the 1; a negative power indicates the number of zeros before the 1, including the zero before the decimal point.

A quantity is said to be written in *scientific notation* when its value is written as a number between 1 and 10, multiplied by 10 raised to some power, multiplied by an appropriate unit. For example, the diameter of the Earth is about 12 760 kilometres; in scientific notation this could be written 1.276×10^4 km. One advantage of scientific notation is that it allows us to indicate the precision claimed for a given quantity. Stating that the Earth's diameter is 1.276×10^4 km really only claims that the diameter is somewhere between 12 755 kilometres and 12 765 kilometres. Had we been confident that the Earth's diameter was 12 760 kilometres, to the nearest kilometre, we should have written 1.2760×10^4 km. The meaningful digits in a number are called **significant figures**. (Significant figures do not include any zeros to the left of the first non-zero digit, so 0.0025 has *two* significant figures, for example.) One advantage of writing numerical values in scientific notation is, therefore, that all the digits in the number that multiplies the power of ten are *significant* figures.

As the course progresses, we will introduce the units in which physical quantities are generally measured. For example, time is measured in seconds, length in metres, energy in joules and electric current in amperes. A detailed understanding of these units is not needed yet, and would make a rather dull start to the course. In the few places where units appear in this book, please skip past them if the meaning is unclear.

Many physical quantities span vast ranges of magnitude. Figures 0.1 and 0.2 use images to indicate the range of lengths and times that are of importance in physics.

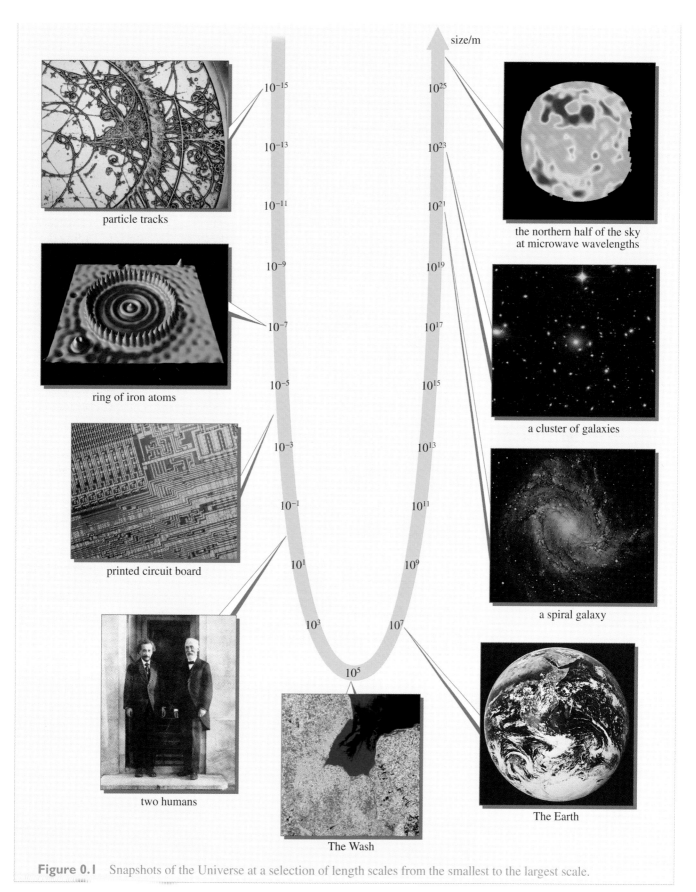

size/m

10^{-15}

10^{-13}

10^{-11}

10^{-9}

10^{-7}

10^{-5}

10^{-3}

10^{-1}

10^{1}

10^{3}

10^{5}

10^{7}

10^{9}

10^{11}

10^{13}

10^{15}

10^{17}

10^{19}

10^{21}

10^{23}

10^{25}

particle tracks

ring of iron atoms

printed circuit board

two humans

The Wash

the northern half of the sky
at microwave wavelengths

a cluster of galaxies

a spiral galaxy

The Earth

Figure 0.1   Snapshots of the Universe at a selection of length scales from the smallest to the largest scale.

Figure 0.2 A range of time scales of relevance to the Universe. Time is measured in billions of years since the Big Bang. The evolution of the Universe is marked by the onset of various ages: from the appearance of particles and galaxies to the emergence of life and intelligence.

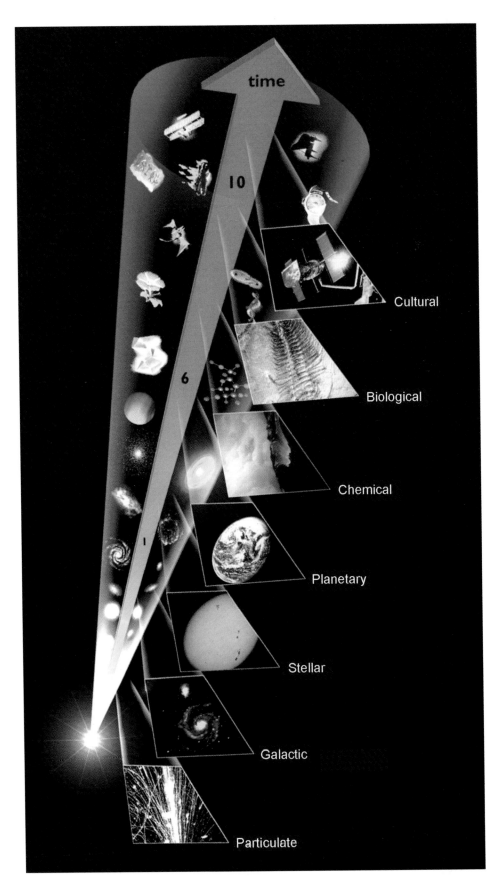

World-views

1 The lawful Universe

1.1 Science and regularity

'Our experience shows that only a small part of the physical Universe needs to be studied in order to elucidate its underlying themes and patterns of behaviour. At root this is what it means for there to exist laws of Nature, and it is why they are invaluable to us. They may allow an understanding of the whole Universe to be built up from the study of small selected parts of it.'

John D. Barrow (1988), *The World Within the World*, Oxford.

Science, it is widely agreed, originated from two main sources. One was the need to develop practical knowledge and to pass it from generation to generation. The other was a more spiritual concern with the nature and origin of the world. Common to both of these well-springs of science was an appreciation of the regularity of Nature. The way to build an arch that would not fall down today was to build it in much the same way as an arch that had not fallen down yesterday. The way to predict the waxing and waning of the Moon this month was to assume that it would follow much the same course as the waxing and waning that had been observed last month and the month before.

The observation of regularity in Nature allows *predictions* to be made concerning the future course of particular events. In many primitive societies these regularities were ascribed to the activities of gods or other mystical spirits. However, gradually, over a long period of time, there emerged the notion that the behaviour of the world was guided by a set of *natural laws* that were themselves regular, in the sense that identical situations could be expected to have identical outcomes.

One of the first scientists to make frequent use of the concept of a law of Nature, in the sense that we now use that term, was the Franciscan friar and scholar Roger Bacon (*c.* 1214–1292). Bacon is traditionally credited with the invention of the magnifying glass, but he is best remembered as an effective advocate of the *scientific method* and a follower of the maxim 'Cease to be ruled by dogmas and authorities; look at the world!' He lived at a time when the commonly accepted view of the world was fundamentally religious, and the Catholic church to which he belonged was coming to embrace the authority of the ancient Greek philosopher Aristotle on matters pertaining to physics and astronomy. Bacon's independence of mind brought him into conflict with the church, and he suffered fifteen years of imprisonment for heresy. Nonetheless, he helped to prepare the way for those who, irrespective of their own religious beliefs, insisted that the scientific investigation of Nature should be rooted in experiment and conducted on a purely rational basis, without reference to dogmatic authority.

Laws of Nature are now a central part of science. Carefully defined concepts, often expressed in mathematical terms, are related by natural laws which are themselves often expressed in a mathematical form. Just what those laws are is a central concern of physicists, who see their branch of science as the one most directly concerned with discovering and applying the fundamental laws of Nature. Improvements in our knowledge of natural laws have repeatedly led to a broadening and a deepening of our understanding of the physical world and hence to a change in the scientific world-view. However, the fundamental requirement that the laws should be rational and rooted in experiment has survived all changes to the detailed content of those laws.

Figure 1.1 Roger Bacon.

1.2 Mathematics and quantification

Roger Bacon once said 'Mathematics is the door and the key to the sciences'. This statement aptly summarizes the role of mathematics in science, particularly in physics, and it is not hard to see why.

Much of physics is concerned with things that can be measured and quantified, that is, expressed as numbers, multiplied by an appropriate unit of measurement such as a metre or a second. It is natural to turn to mathematics to try to reveal patterns underlying such measured data. This is more than a matter of arithmetic. By Roger Bacon's time the basic ideas of *algebra* had been developed, mainly by Arabic mathematicians and astronomers. The idea of *representing* a quantity by a symbol, such as x or t is extremely powerful because it allows us to express general relationships in a very compact way. For example, in the equation

$$h = \tfrac{1}{2} g t^2, \tag{1.1}$$

the symbol h represents the height fallen by an object that has been dropped from rest, the symbol t represents the time the object has been falling, and g is a constant with a known value ($g = 9.81$ metres per second per second). Equation 1.1 encapsulates a wealth of information about falling objects, information that is precise and useful. The tools of algebra allow us to go further. For example, the above equation can be rearranged to read

$$t = \sqrt{\frac{2h}{g}}, \tag{1.2}$$

so now, if we know the height fallen by an object, we can work out how long it has taken to fall.

Mathematics provides a natural medium for rational argument. Given an equation that relates various quantities, the rules of mathematics allow that equation to be re-expressed in a number of different but logically equivalent ways, all of which are valid if the original equation was valid. Given two equations, mathematical reasoning allows them to be combined to produce new equations which are again valid if the original equations were valid. Long chains of reasoning can be put together in this way, all of which are guaranteed to be correct provided that the starting points are correct and no mathematical rules are transgressed. Quite often these arguments are so long and detailed that it would be impossible to follow them in ordinary language, even if it were possible to express them at all.

Mathematics has been an immensely effective part of the scientist's toolkit throughout history. It was the increased use of mathematics in the sixteenth and seventeenth centuries, in the hands of individuals such as Galileo Galilei (1564–1642) and Isaac Newton (1642–1727), that opened a new era of physics and marked one of the greatest flowerings of science. Galileo and Newton, it should be noted, were both, at key times in their careers, professors of mathematics. In both cases they brought mathematical precision and rigour to the study of science, and in Newton's case made major breakthroughs in mathematics in the process. The types of mathematics used in physics are extremely varied. Practically every branch of mathematics that has developed over the centuries has been used within physics. Sometimes physics has provided direct inspiration for new mathematical concepts, sometimes abstract mathematical theories have found completely unexpected uses in physics, years after their introduction as products of pure thought.

Despite its power, physics students often find the extensive use of mathematics troublesome and some think of mathematics as providing a barrier to understanding. Do not let this happen to you. From the outset, you should regard mathematics as a friend rather than a foe. As the course progresses, you may meet some mathematical ideas that are new to you, or you may need to improve your ability to use methods you have met before. These are not distractions from trying to understand physics, but are the tools needed to make that understanding possible. It is only through using mathematics that a secure understanding can be achieved. When you see an equation, welcome its concision and clarity and try to 'read' the equation just as you would the large number of words it replaces. Learn to get beneath the squiggles and the equals sign and to understand the quantitative assertion that is being made.

Figure 1.2 "I see through your squiggles."

Later, you will see how graphs can be used to visualize an equation and how consideration of special cases and trends can help unpack its meaning.

Question 1.1 When Jesuits first visited China they spoke about the 'laws of science'. The Chinese thought this was a ridiculous notion: people could be persuaded to obey the laws of the Emperor, but sticks and stones have no intelligence so it is absurd to think of them as 'obeying laws'. How would you respond to this? ■

2   The clockwork Universe

2.1   Mechanics and determinism

It is probably fair to say that no single individual has had a greater influence on the scientific view of the world than Isaac Newton. The main reason for Newton's prominence was his own intrinsic genius, but another important factor was the particular state of knowledge when he was, in his own phrase, 'in the prime of my age for invention'.

In 1543, a century before Newton's birth, Nicolaus Copernicus launched a scientific revolution by rejecting the prevailing Earth-centred view of the Universe in favour

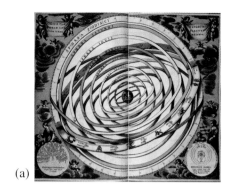
(a)

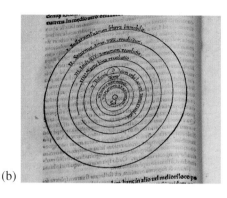
(b)

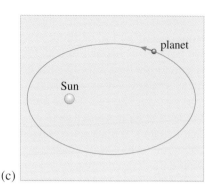
(c)

Figure 1.3 Three views of planetary motion. (a) The Earth-centred view of the ancient Greeks and of the Catholic church in the sixteenth century. (b) The Copernican system, in which the planets move in collections of circles around the Sun. (c) The Keplerian system in which a planet follows an elliptical orbit, with the Sun at one focus of the ellipse.

of a **heliocentric** view in which the Earth moved round the Sun. By removing the Earth, and with it humankind, from the centre of creation, Copernicus had set the scene for a number of confrontations between the Catholic church and some of its more independently minded followers. The most famous of these must surely have been Galileo, who was summoned to appear before the Inquisition in 1633, on a charge of heresy, for supporting Copernicus' ideas. As a result Galileo was 'shown the instruments of torture', and invited to renounce his declared opinion that the Earth moves around the Sun. This he did, though tradition has it that at the end of his renunciation he muttered '*Eppur si muove*' ('And yet it moves').

In the Protestant countries of Northern Europe, thought on astronomical matters was more free, and it was there in the early seventeenth century, that the German-born astronomer Johannes Kepler (1571–1630) devised a modified form of Copernicanism that was in good agreement with the best observational data available at the time. According to Kepler, the planets *did* move around the Sun, but their orbital paths were ellipses rather than collections of circles. This discovery, first published in 1609 in Kepler's book *Astronomia Nova* (The New Astronomy), was essentially an observational result. Kepler had no real reason to *expect* that the planets would move in ellipses, though he did speculate that they might be impelled by some kind of magnetic influence emanating from the Sun.

Kepler's ideas were underpinned by new discoveries in mathematics. Chief among these was the realization, by René Descartes, that problems in geometry can be recast as problems in algebra. Like most revolutionary ideas, the concept is disarmingly simple. Imagine a giant grid extending over the whole of space. Figure 1.4 shows the two-dimensional case, with a grid extending over part of the page. The grid is calibrated (in centimetres) so the position of any point can be specified by giving its x- and y-coordinates on the grid. For example, the coordinates of point A are $x = 3$ cm and $y = 4$ cm.

This idea becomes more powerful when we consider lines and geometrical shapes. The straight line shown in Figure 1.5 is characterized by the fact that, at each point along the line, the y-coordinate is half the x-coordinate. Thus, the x- and y- coordinates of each point on the line obey the equation $y = 0.5x$, and this is said to be the equation of the line. Similarly, the circle in Figure 1.5 is characterized by the equation $\sqrt{x^2 + y^2} = 2$ cm. This is the beginning of a branch of mathematics, called *coordinate geometry*, which represents geometrical shapes by equations, and which establishes geometrical truths by combining and rearranging those equations. Sometimes, what is difficult to show using traditional geometry is easy to establish using algebra, so this 'mapping' of geometry into algebra gave scientists new ways of tackling geometrical problems, allowing them to go further than the greatest mathematicians of ancient Greece.

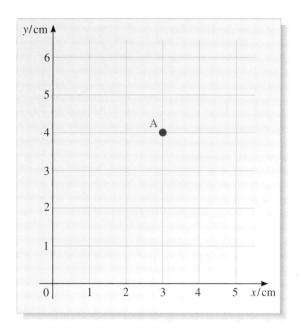

Figure 1.4   A two-dimensional coordinate system can be used to locate the position of any point in terms of its *x*- and *y*-coordinates.

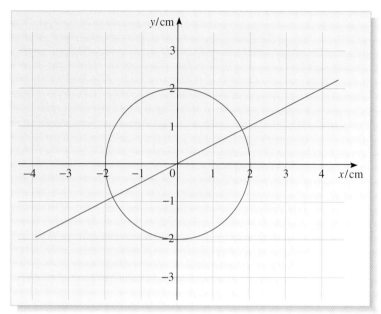

Figure 1.5   A two-dimensional coordinate system can be used to represent lines and other geometrical shapes by equations.

Newton's good fortune was to be active in physics (or 'natural philosophy' as it would then have been called) at a time when the cause of Kepler's ellipses was still unexplained and the tools of geometry were ripe for exploitation. The physics of Aristotle was clearly inadequate, and all other attempts seemed unconvincing. The new astronomy called for a new physics which Newton had the ability and the opportunity to devise. He was the right man, in the right place, at the right time.

Isaac Newton (1642–1727)

Isaac Newton was born on Christmas Day 1642 at Woolsthorp in Lincolnshire, England. His father had died a few months before the birth and Newton himself was born so prematurely that it was thought he might not survive. Newton was partly brought up by his grandmother, and seems not to have had a close relationship with his mother. He exhibited no great talent at school, but managed to avoid the task of managing his mother's farmlands and became instead an undergraduate at Trinity College in the University of Cambridge.

As a student Newton read the works of Aristotle and was taught mathematics, as was customary, but he also taught himself physics and thus became acquainted with the works of Galileo and Kepler, amongst others. He graduated in 1665, by which time he had already started to break new ground in mathematics. Due to an outbreak of plague, the University of Cambridge was closed

for much of the next two years and Newton spent most of his time back at Woolsthorp. It was during this period that he made many of his greatest breakthroughs, or at least laid their foundations. Over an eighteen month period he:

- made fundamental advances in mathematics (essentially creating the subject of *calculus*, which has become a major part of the language of physics);

- used a glass prism to demonstrate that white light is actually a mixture of colours;

- began to consider the possibility that gravity, which obviously influenced bodies close to the Earth, might be a universal phenomenon holding the Moon in its orbit around the Earth and the Earth in its orbit around the Sun.

Following the reopening of the University, Newton returned to Trinity College where he became a Fellow in 1667. Two years later, still only 26, he was appointed Lucasian Professor of Mathematics on the recommendation of his predecessor, Isaac Barrow.

Figure 1.6 Isaac Newton.

Figure 1.7 Woolsthorp Manor —
Newton's birthplace.

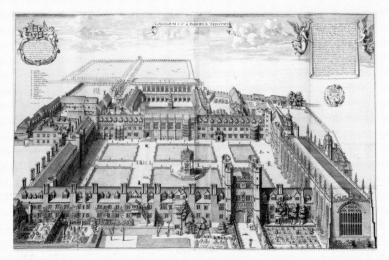

Figure 1.8 Trinity College, Cambridge around 1690.

In addition to combining mathematical genius and profound physical insight, Newton also possessed practical skills. He built the furnaces in his own small laboratory in Trinity College, where he personally carried out alchemical experiments. He also constructed a novel kind of reflecting telescope, for which he was elected a Fellow of the Royal Society. However, Newton was a solitary and difficult person who has often been described as neurotic. He reacted badly to criticism and expected to get full credit for his discoveries even though he often did little to publicize them. He became involved in a number of bitter disputes over priority. Newton also harboured unconventional religious views (he was essentially a Unitarian) which prevented him from becoming the Master of his college. In 1678 he apparently suffered a nervous breakdown and for several years thereafter concentrated on alchemy and scriptural studies.

Newton was recalled to natural philosophy in 1684 by the young astronomer Edmond Halley who asked how a planet would move if it was attracted towards the Sun by a force that weakened in proportion to the inverse square of its distance from the Sun: in symbols, force $\propto 1/(\text{distance})^2$. (This means, for example, that increasing the distance by a factor of three decreases the force by a factor of *nine*.) Newton is said to have immediately told Halley the answer (an ellipse) having worked it out during the plague years. Halley persuaded Newton to recreate his calculations and publish them. The result, in 1686, was what is widely regarded as the most influential book in the history of science, Newton's *Philosophiae Naturalis Principia Mathematica* (Mathematical Principles of Natural Philosophy), a work usually referred to simply as *Principia*. In the opening pages of this book, Newton presented his definitions of force and mass, and his three laws of motion. He then went on to demonstrate that a body attracted towards a fixed point by a force that varied in proportion to the inverse square of its distance from that point would, in many circumstances, follow an elliptical path. After establishing many other results Newton presented, in Part 3 of the book, his *System of the World* in which he proposed that gravity was a universal force, acting between *any* two particles of matter, with a magnitude that is proportional to the product of their masses and the inverse square of their separation — just the kind of inverse square law that Halley had asked about. Thus Newton was able to explain the observed motion of the planets. He went on to consider the Moon's motion in detail (taking account of the gravitational influence of both the Earth and the Sun), the behaviour of comets, and the gravitational origin of the Earth's oceanic tides. The scope and power of *Principia* caused a sensation, and made Newton the foremost scientist of his time, or perhaps any time.

Newton suffered another breakdown in 1693 and subsequently quit Cambridge and the academic life in favour of London and the world of affairs. He became Warden of the Mint in 1696 and successfully oversaw the introduction of a new coinage. As a consequence he was appointed to a lucrative position as Master of the Mint and devoted much of his remaining time to theology and biblical chronology. He was elected President of the Royal Society in 1703, published his last great scientific work *Opticks* in 1704 (based on work performed many years earlier), and was knighted in 1705. He died, in London in 1727, and is buried in Westminster Abbey.

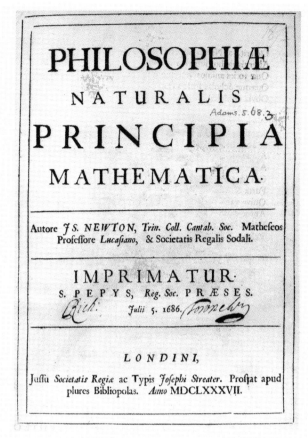

Figure 1.9   *Principia* — Newton's masterpiece.

For years before Newton, people had been trying to understand the world from a scientific perspective, discovering laws that would help explain why things happen in the way that they do. Bits of knowledge were assembled, but there was no clear idea how these bits related to one another; understanding was fragmentary. Newton's great achievement was to provide a synthesis of scientific knowledge. He did not claim to have all the answers, but he discovered a convincing quantitative framework that seemed to underlie everything else. For the first time, scientists felt they understood the fundamentals, and it seemed that future advances would merely fill in the details of Newton's grand vision. Before Newton, few could have imagined that such a world-view would be possible. Later generations looked back with envy at Newton's good fortune. As the great Italian–French scientist Joseph Lagrange remarked:

'There is only one Universe … It can happen to only one man in the world's history to be the interpreter of its laws.'

At the core of Newton's world-view is the belief that all the motion we see around us can be explained in terms of a single set of laws. We cannot give the details of these laws now, but it is appropriate to mention three key points:

1   Newton concentrated not so much on motion, as on *deviation from steady motion* — deviation that occurs, for example, when an object speeds up, or slows down, or veers off in a new direction.

2   Wherever deviation from steady motion occurred, Newton looked for a cause. Slowing down, for example, might be caused by braking. He described such a cause as a force. We are all familiar with the idea of applying a force, whenever we use our muscles to push or pull anything.

3   Finally Newton produced a quantitative link between force and deviation from steady motion and, at least in the case of gravity, quantified the force by proposing his famous law of universal gravitation.

In keeping with his grand vision, Newton proposed just one law for gravity — a law that worked for every scrap of matter in the Universe, for moons and planets as well as for apples and the Earth. By combining this law with his general laws of motion, Newton was able to demonstrate mathematically that a single planet would move around the Sun in an elliptical orbit, just as Kepler claimed each of the planets did. Moreover, thanks to the understanding that gravity was the cause of planetary motion, Newtonian physics was able to predict that gravitational attractions between the planets would cause small departures from the purely elliptical motion that Kepler had described. In this way, Newton was able to explain Kepler's results and to go beyond them.

Books 2 and 3 give a thorough discussion of mechanics.

In the hands of Newton's successors, notably the French scientist Pierre Simon Laplace (1749–1827), Newton's discoveries became the basis for a detailed and comprehensive study of **mechanics** (the study of force and motion). The upshot of all this was a mechanical world-view that regarded the Universe as something that unfolded according to mathematical laws with all the precision and inevitability of a well-made clock. The detailed character of the Newtonian laws was such that once this majestic clockwork had been set in motion, its future development was, in principle, entirely predictable. This property of Newtonian mechanics is called **determinism**. It had an enormously important implication. Given an accurate description of the character, position and velocity of every particle in the Universe at some particular moment (i.e. the *initial condition* of the Universe), and an understanding of the forces that operated between those particles, the subsequent development of the Universe could be predicted with as much accuracy as desired.

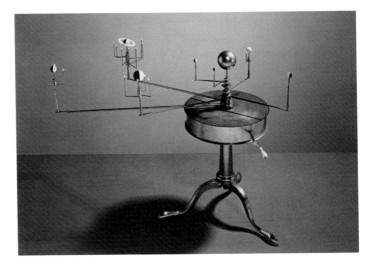

Figure 1.10 An orrery (a mechanical model of the Solar System) can be taken as a metaphor for the clockwork Universe of Newtonian mechanics.

Needless to say, obtaining a completely detailed description of the entire Universe at any one time was not a realistic undertaking, nor was solving all the equations required to predict its future course. But that wasn't the point. It was enough that the future was ordained. If you accepted the proposition that humans were entirely physical systems, composed of particles of matter obeying physical laws of motion, then in principle, every future human action would be already determined by the past. For some this was the ultimate indication of God: where there was a design there must be a Designer, where there was a clock there must have been a Clockmaker. For others it was just the opposite, a denial of the doctrine of **free will** which asserts that human beings are free to determine their own actions. Even for those without religious convictions, the notion that our every thought and action was pre-determined in principle, even if unpredictable in practice, made the Newtonian Universe seem strangely discordant with our everyday experience of the vagaries of human life.

Question 1.2   In principle, according to Newtonian mechanics, it is possible to predict the entire future behaviour of the Universe provided the initial positions and velocities of all the particles in it are known, and the laws describing their interactions are known. List at least two reasons why this goal is, in practice, beyond our reach. ■

2.2 Energy and conservation

Newtonian mechanics is concerned with explaining motion, yet it contains within it the much simpler idea that some things never change. Take the concept of mass, for example, which appears throughout Newtonian mechanics, including the law of gravitation. In Newtonian mechanics, mass is conserved. This means that the mass of the Universe is constant and the mass of any specified collection of particles is constant, no matter how much rearrangement occurs within the system. A chemist might take one kilogram of hydrogen and let it react with eight kilograms of oxygen to produce water. According to the **law of conservation of mass**, nine kilograms of water will be produced, the same as the total mass of the ingredients (1 kg + 8 kg = 9 kg). You may think this is trivial, but it is not. **Conservation laws** are rare and wonderful things. There is no general law of conservation of volume for example. The initial volume of the hydrogen and oxygen is far greater than the final volume of the water. The fact that mass is conserved really is a deep discovery about the checks and balances that exist in our Universe.

The conservation of energy is dealt with in detail in Book 3.

Newtonian mechanics introduced several other important conservation laws, including the celebrated **law of conservation of energy**. Not too surprisingly, this law states that the total energy of the Universe is constant and the total energy of an isolated system of particles is constant. But the full meaning of these words will only become apparent once the concept of energy has been properly defined.

For the moment, it is sufficient to note that we all have some familiarity with the concept of energy. We pay money for gas, electricity and petrol precisely because they are sources of energy, and we use that energy to heat and light our homes and to drive cars. From this, it is apparent that energy has many different forms — chemical energy in gas or electrical energy can be converted into light energy, thermal energy, or the energy of a whirring vacuum cleaner. It is possible to change energy from one form into another but, crucially, when all these forms are properly quantified, the total amount of energy remains constant. Energy is neither created or destroyed because it is a conserved quantity.

Perhaps the simplest form of energy is **kinetic energy**: the energy associated with motion. If a particle has mass m and speed v, its kinetic energy is given by the formula

$$E = \tfrac{1}{2}mv^2. \tag{1.3}$$

Suppose the particle hits a wall and is brought to a sudden halt. It then has no speed and no kinetic energy, but the initial energy has not been lost. Rather, it has been converted into other forms of energy, such as those associated with sound and heat.

The conservation of energy can be illustrated by considering a stone that is thrown vertically upwards. The stone starts out with a certain amount of kinetic energy, but as it climbs it slows down and its kinetic energy decreases. What happens to this energy? The answer is that there is another form of energy called **potential energy**, which in this case is associated with the downward pull of gravity and increases as the stone climbs. On the upward part of its journey, the stone's kinetic energy is gradually converted into potential energy until, at the top of its flight, the stone is momentarily at rest. At this point, the stone has no kinetic energy and its potential energy is at its highest. On the way down, potential energy is converted back into kinetic energy, as the stone loses height and gains speed. Assuming that no other forms of energy are involved, by the time the stone returns to its initial height, all of its initial kinetic energy is recovered and the stone is once again travelling at its initial speed. Figure 1.11 shows how the kinetic and potential energies of the stone vary during its up-and-down flight. The total energy, formed by adding the kinetic and potential energies together, is also shown. You can see quite clearly that energy is converted from one form to another while the total energy remains fixed.

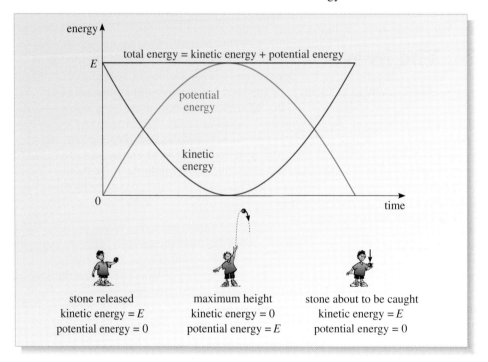

Figure 1.11   A stone is thrown vertically upwards and falls down again. The graph shows how the kinetic energy, potential energy and total energy vary as a stone travels up and down again. (For convenience, the potential energy is taken to be zero when the stone is launched, and when it is caught again.)

One of the consequences of the conservation of energy is that it makes sense to think of storing energy in order to have a ready supply whenever required. Figure 1.12 shows several examples of energy storage in action.

(a)

(b)

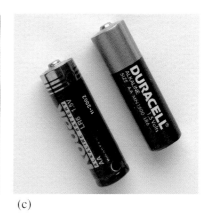
(c)

Figure 1.12   Some examples of energy storage. (a) A hydroelectric scheme in which the gravitational potential energy of water descending from a high lake is used to drive generators that produce electricity. (b) Petrol, a liquid from which it is easy to extract chemical energy. (c) An electrical dry cell which stores electrical energy.

3   The irreversible Universe

'Science owes more to the steam engine than the steam engine owes to Science.'

L. J. Henderson (1917)

From the time of Newton till the end of the nineteenth century the development of physics consisted essentially of the refinement and extension of the mechanical view of the Universe. There were many stages in this process but one of the most interesting came towards its end with the realization that the cosmic clockwork was inevitably unwinding and running down. The source of this realization was the development of thermodynamics.

3.1   Thermodynamics and entropy

The first half of the nineteenth century was a period of great economic and industrial growth. The steam engine, invented in the previous century, was becoming increasingly common in locomotives, mines and factories; power was becoming available on demand. A major priority for engineers was to produce more efficient engines, in order to deliver more useful power for less expenditure on fuel. **Thermodynamics** emerged as a study of the basic principles determining energy flows and the efficiency of machines.

This may seem like a big idea in engineering rather than a big idea in physics. Certainly, thermodynamics is important to engineers, and continues to guide the design of engines of all sorts, but thermodynamics is just as important to physicists. It explains a wealth of natural phenomena, from the freezing of water to the evaporation of a black hole, and casts light on concepts like temperature, heat and spontaneous processes, which do not fit naturally into the Newtonian world-view.

It is still instructive to return to the origins of the subject. Speaking very roughly, a steam engine is a device which uses fuel to convert water into steam and uses the resulting expansion in volume to drive a piston. The kinetic energy of the piston is exploited using a variety of mechanical devices — gears, drive belts, camshafts and so on, but thermodynamics concentrates on the early stages of the process, where heat is used to create kinetic energy.

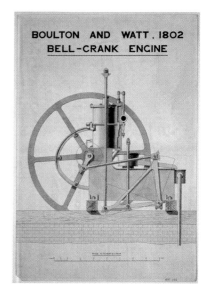

Figure 1.13   A steam engine, in which energy stored in coal is used to create heat to vaporize water. The resulting increase in volume drives a piston, so allowing useful work to be done.

To begin with there was much dispute about the nature of heat. Many people thought of it as a sort of fluid which could flow from one body to another. Eventually, it became clear that no such fluid exists and that **heat** is best defined as energy transferred because of a temperature difference. This scientific definition of the word 'heat' is slightly different from everyday usage, so it may help to consider a specific example. Think of a hot steak (veggie-burger, if you prefer) resting on a cold plate. The steak cools down and the plate warms up as energy flows from the steak to the plate. The energy transferred in this way is called heat. By contrast, **work** is energy transferred by non-thermal means. For example, if you rub the plate vigorously with a cloth, the energy of the plate will increase and it will get slightly warmer. But, this energy transfer is not *caused* by a temperature difference between the plate and the cloth, so energy transferred by rubbing is classified as work rather than heat.

In general, the total energy gained by a system (such as the plate) is the sum of the heat *and* the work transferred to it. It is worth emphasizing that heat and work are not themselves properties of a system. We cannot examine a plate and deduce that it has received so much energy from heat and so much energy from work. All that counts is that the plate *has* a total amount of energy, and that any increase in this energy is the sum of the heat and work transferred to the plate. This understanding of heat, work and energy is incorporated in the first law of thermodynamics.

> **First law of thermodynamics**
> When all types of energy transfer, including work and heat, are taken into account, the energy of an isolated system remains constant.

From a modern perspective, we can see that this is just another way of stating the law of conservation of energy with the explicit recognition of heat as a quantity of energy to be included, alongside work, in any energy audit. Inventors should take note: an engine may convert energy from one form to another, but it cannot produce energy from nothing. The kinetic energy of the piston of a steam engine, for instance, has been paid for in advance by the heat transferred to the steam.

Given this modern understanding of heat as energy transferred in a particular way, you might wonder why we bother to distinguish between heat and work at all. The reason is that heat can be used to define another important quantity: **entropy**.

Book 4 will discuss heat, temperature and entropy.

We cannot define entropy properly in this introductory survey. In very broad terms you can think of entropy as a measure of 'disorder' — the random motion of molecules in steam corresponds to more disorder, and hence more entropy, than the more orderly motion of molecules in ice. Interestingly enough, there is a connection between entropy and heat: whenever heat is transferred to a body, the entropy of that body increases. In the simplest case, if a small amount of heat Q is transferred gently to a body, whilst the temperature of the body is T, the entropy of the body increases by Q/T.

The term entropy was deliberately chosen to be reminiscent of energy, though the differences between the two quantities are just as important as their similarities. Entropy and energy are similar in that an isolated body may be said to have a certain 'entropy content' just as it may be said to have a certain 'energy content'. However, while the first law of thermodynamics ensures that the energy of an isolated system is always conserved, the second law of thermodynamics makes a slightly weaker assertion about entropy:

> **Second law of thermodynamics**
> The total entropy of an isolated system cannot decrease; it may (and generally does) increase.

The requirement that the total entropy should not decrease has the effect of ruling out enormous numbers of processes that are perfectly consistent with energy conservation. When heat flows between a steak and a plate there is no violation of energy conservation; the energy lost by the steak is gained by the plate. However, conservation of energy does not explain why the heat always flows *from* the hot steak *to* the cold plate; this is where the second law of thermodynamics comes in. Suppose the steak is at temperature T, the plate is at a slightly lower temperature $0.95T$, and that a small amount of heat Q is transferred from the steak to the plate. Then the entropy of the steak decreases by Q/T while the entropy of the plate increases by $Q/0.95T$. It is easy to see that the entropy lost by the steak is smaller than the entropy gained by the plate, so the total entropy of the Universe has increased; this process is therefore consistent with the second law of thermodynamics. If, on the other hand, heat Q had flowed from the cold plate to the hot steak, the entropy lost by the plate ($Q/0.95T$) would have been greater than the entropy gained by the steak (Q/T), and the total entropy of the Universe would have decreased. This violates the second law of thermodynamics, so we can be sure that the process is impossible. Heat flow is said to be an *irreversible* process — you will never see heat flowing spontaneously from a cold body to a hotter one.

Whenever energy is transferred or transformed, the final entropy of the Universe must be at least as high as the initial entropy. This usually means that heat flows are required to ensure that the total entropy does not decrease. Inventors should again take note. In most engines, heat is an unwanted by-product: the real aim is to transfer energy as work, perhaps to propel a vehicle or lift a weight. Since part of the energy initially stored in the fuel is inevitably wasted as heat, only a fraction is left to do useful work. Thus, thermodynamics imposes fundamental limits on the *efficiency* of engines. Fortunately, it also suggests ways of increasing efficiency, explaining for example, why a diesel engine is likely to be more efficient than a petrol engine, a topic we will return to in Book 4.

Question 1.3   When a room-temperature object is placed in a refrigerator, heat flows out of the object and its entropy decreases. Indeed, the refrigerator may be said to be a device for sucking entropy out of warm objects. How can such a decrease in entropy be consistent with the second law of thermodynamics?   ■

3.2 Equilibrium and irreversibility

As the science of thermodynamics developed beyond its industrial roots, two powerful ideas came to the fore — **equilibrium** and **irreversibility**. These ideas were already implicit in studies of heat. You have already seen that heat flow from a hot steak to a cold plate is an irreversible process. The effect of this process is to cool down the hot steak and warm up the cold plate, leading to a more uniform distribution of temperature. The heat transfer continues until a state of equilibrium is reached, characterized by a completely uniform temperature.

Understanding the conditions needed for equilibrium, and the irreversible processes that drive systems towards equilibrium, has deep consequences throughout the sciences. For example, under normal conditions, the equilibrium state of carbon is graphite, rather than diamond. Fortunately, the processes that restore equilibrium are very slow in this case, so diamonds do not perceptibly turn into graphite. But, under some rather extreme conditions, diamond is the equilibrium state rather than graphite, and this fact can be used to create new diamonds from soot. More generally, thermodynamics determines which states of matter are in equilibrium under any given set of conditions.

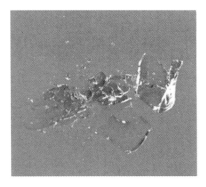

Figure 1.14 Some examples of irreversibility: (a) a smashed glass, (b) an omelette.

Entropy and the second law of thermodynamics provide the key to understanding equilibrium. An isolated system, free from all other influences, may undergo various spontaneous changes, some of which will increase its entropy. If the total entropy *increases* during a process, as it usually does, the process is irreversible — it is impossible to return to the starting point, leaving no other traces, since that would require a decrease in the total entropy, which is impossible. Once the entropy has increased, it cannot decrease again. An isolated system therefore approaches a state in which the entropy has the highest possible value. This is a state of equilibrium. In equilibrium, the entropy of the system cannot increase (because it is already at a maximum) and it cannot decrease (because that would violate the second law of thermodynamics). The only changes allowed are those in which the entropy remains constant. This equilibrium can be disturbed if the system is allowed to interact with its surroundings. The entropy of the system may then decrease, *provided* the entropy of the surroundings increases by at least as much, ensuring that there is no decrease in the entropy of the Universe as a whole.

If we start with a system that is close to, but has not quite reached, equilibrium, thermodynamics can suggest which processes will increase the entropy and lead towards equilibrium. Heat transfers are one source of entropy changes, but there are others. If you take two different gases and allow them to mix together in a flask that is so well insulated that no heat can be transferred to or from the flask, the entropy of the mixture turns out to be greater than the entropy of the two separate gases. That is why the mixing is an irreversible process. Once mixed, the gases will not spontaneously separate. Similar considerations explain why a dropped glass can shatter into a thousand fragments, but a thousand fragments will never spontaneously form themselves into a glass. Also, an egg can be made into an omelette, but an omelette will not make itself into an egg. There *is* an 'arrow of time' that points from the past to the future, and tomorrow *will* be different from today.

If these ideas are correct, the Universe must be inescapably and irreversibly approaching a state in which its entropy has the highest possible value. This will be a state of equilibrium for the Universe as a whole, where all the fuel will have been expended and the temperature will be uniform, leaving no prospect of generating heat flows and extracting useful work. In a phrase made popular in the 1930s by the Cambridge cosmologist Sir Arthur Eddington, the Universe is said to be approaching a final state of 'heat death'. In this sense, the clockwork of the Newtonian Universe is running down.

3.3 Statistical mechanics

You saw earlier that very strong claims were made for Newtonian mechanics. Many regarded it as a basic framework that would underlie all scientific explanations. It is therefore natural to ask about the relationship between Newtonian mechanics and thermodynamics:

● Do they contradict one another?

● Are they separate aspects of the truth?

● Can thermodynamics be derived from Newtonian mechanics?

These are not easy questions. Thermodynamics was specifically designed to deal with concepts like temperature, heat and entropy which had no clear Newtonian interpretation. The gulf between the two subjects can be illustrated by taking, say, a glass of water in a state of equilibrium. We now know that this contains an *enormous* number of molecules (roughly 10^{24}), each feeling electrical forces due to other molecules and moving rapidly around, colliding with other molecules in the liquid and the glass. The Newtonian world-view would require us to keep track of each and every molecule, building up an immensely complicated and detailed description. Of course, this is utterly beyond our powers. Even if it were possible, the results would provide little or no insight. It would be like looking at a painting under a microscope when its true significance is only apparent from a distance of a few metres. Thermodynamics adopts a more practical viewpoint. Rather than tracking each water molecule in detail, it uses just a few well-chosen variables — including energy, volume, pressure, temperature and entropy — to characterize the state of the water as a whole. The amazing thing is that this works. The thermodynamic description is massively incomplete, yet it is sufficient to make useful predictions.

There is a special branch of physics, called **statistical mechanics**, which attempts to bridge the gap between descriptions on the scale of molecules and thermodynamics. It recognizes that our knowledge of a complicated system, such as a glass of water, is inevitably incomplete so we are essentially reduced to making guesses. This may seem to be a terrible weakness, but statistical mechanics actually turns it into an advantage. It replaces precise knowledge of the motion of molecules by probabilities indicating how the molecules are likely to move, on average. It then goes on to estimate the probability of measuring a particular pressure, energy or entropy in the system as a whole. This is rather like the trick pulled by opinion pollsters when they predict the result of a general election without knowing how every individual in the country intends to vote. Pollsters have a mixed reputation, but the calculations of statistical mechanics are much more clear cut. They turn out to provide predictions that are *overwhelmingly* likely to happen — so much so, that they appear to be laws of Nature. The second law of thermodynamics is a case in point. From the viewpoint of statistical mechanics, the entropy of the Universe is not bound to increase, it is just overwhelmingly likely to do so. Perhaps 'heat death' will not be the end after all. After countless years of dull uniformity, a very unlikely (but possible) new fluctuation may occur with a lower than maximum entropy, and interesting things will start to happen again.

Figure 1.15 Ludwig Boltzmann (1844–1906).

Boltzmann, entropy and disorder

The statistical interpretation of thermodynamics was pioneered by James Clerk Maxwell (1831–1879) and brought to fruition by the Austrian physicist Ludwig Boltzmann.

In 1877 Boltzmann used statistical ideas to gain valuable insight into the meaning of entropy. He realized that entropy could be thought of as a measure of disorder, and that the second law of thermodynamics expressed the fact that disorder tends to increase. You have probably noticed this tendency in everyday life! However, you might also think that you have the power to step in, rearrange things a bit, and restore order. For example, you might decide to tidy up your wardrobe. Would this lead to a decrease in disorder, and hence a decrease in entropy? Actually, it would not. This is because there are inevitable side-effects: whilst sorting out your clothes, you will be breathing, metabolizing and warming your surroundings. When everything has been taken into account, the total disorder (as measured by the entropy) will have increased, in spite of the admirable state of order in your wardrobe. The second law of

thermodynamics is relentless. The total entropy and the total disorder are overwhelmingly unlikely to decrease.

Boltzmann's contribution was vital, but had a tragic outcome. Towards the end of the nineteenth century several puzzling facts (which eventually led to quantum theory), triggered a reaction against 'materialist' science, and some people even questioned whether atoms exist. Boltzmann, whose work was based on the concept of atoms, found himself cast as their chief defender and the debates became increasingly bitter. Always prone to bouts of depression, Boltzmann came to believe that his life's work had been rejected by the scientific community, although this was far from being true. In 1906, he committed suicide. If despair over rejection, or frustration over being unable to prove his point, were contributing factors the irony would be great indeed. Soon after Boltzmann's death, clinching evidence was found for atoms, and few would ever doubt their existence again.

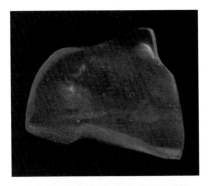

Figure 1.16 Examples of electric and magnetic forces. The ancient Greeks were aware that when samples of amber, which they called ηλεκτρον (electron), were rubbed with wool or fur they acquired the ability to attract light objects such as feathers. They were also aware that the substance we now call lodestone, which could be found in northern Greece in the area known as Magnesia, had the ability to attract pieces of iron.

Books 5 and 6 give a thorough discussion of electromagnetism.

4 The intangible Universe

4.1 Electromagnetism and fields

When Newton wrote about 'The System of the World' in Part 3 of *Principia*, the only forces he could discuss in any detail were the contact forces that arose when one object touched another, and gravity, which acted at a distance. Even so, Newton thought that there were other forces at work in the world, and hoped they might eventually be brought within his overall scheme just as gravity had been. In fact, Newton wrote:

> 'I wish we could derive the rest of the phenomena of Nature by the same kind of reasoning from mechanical principles, for I am induced by many reasons to suspect that they may all depend upon certain forces by which the particles of the bodies, by some causes hitherto unknown, are either mutually impelled towards one another, and cohere in regular figures, or are repelled and recede from one another.'

> Isaac Newton (1686), *Principia*.

Amongst the phenomena familiar to Newton, but which he could not treat mathematically, were those of *electricity* and *magnetism*, both of which had been known since antiquity (Figure 1.16). One of the key concepts that Newton lacked, but which eventually proved to be crucial to the quantification of both electricity and magnetism was that of *electric charge*. This was originally viewed as something like a fluid that could be passed from one object to another, but is now seen, rather like mass, as a fundamental attribute of matter. Just as Newton had been able to make gravity an effective part of the mechanistic world-view by declaring that the gravitational force between two point-like bodies was proportional to the product of their masses and the inverse square of their separation, so the French scientist Charles Coulomb (1736–1806) was able to do the same for electricity by showing that the electrical force between two point-like bodies was proportional to the product of their charges and the inverse square of their separation. In terms of symbols, this can be expressed as:

NEWTON	COULOMB
$F_{\text{grav}} \propto \dfrac{m_1 m_2}{r^2}$	$F_{\text{elec}} \propto \dfrac{q_1 q_2}{r^2}$.

However, electrical charge can be positive or negative, and the electrical forces can be attractive or repulsive in accordance with the famous dictum 'like charges repel; unlike charges attract'. Forces between magnets could be treated in a similar way by using north and south magnetic poles in place of positive and negative charges.

The incorporation of electrical and magnetic forces into the mechanistic world-view appeared to be a triumphant vindication of Newton's foresight. But it was really only the beginning of a story, not the end of one. Subsequent investigations were to show that an *electric* current — a flow of charge — could produce a *magnetic* force. This showed that the apparently separate subjects of electricity and magnetism were actually different aspects of a single subject: **electromagnetism**. It was within this unified subject that a new physical concept was to arise, that of a **field**. The field concept was destined to play an enormously important role in reshaping the physicist's view of the world. It would initially augment the mechanistic world-view, then around 1900, come to rival it, and ultimately, after 1926, play an important part in its downfall.

The field theory of electromagnetism was mainly the creation of two men, Michael Faraday and James Clerk Maxwell. They are, in a sense, the Galileo and the Newton of field theory.

Michael Faraday (1791–1867)

Michael Faraday was the son of a blacksmith. Apprenticed to a bookbinder at 14, he read about science, became enthralled with the subject, secured a job as a laboratory assistant at the Royal Institution in London, and eventually rose to be the Institution's Director and one of the most accomplished experimental researchers of all time. Amongst his many achievements, he is credited with the construction of the first electric motor and the discovery of both the principle and the method whereby a rotating magnet can be used to create an electric current in a coil of wire (still the basis of modern electricity generating plants). Faraday never became a very able mathematician, and it was his profoundly physical way of viewing the world that led him to create the concept of a field.

Figure 1.17   Michael Faraday.

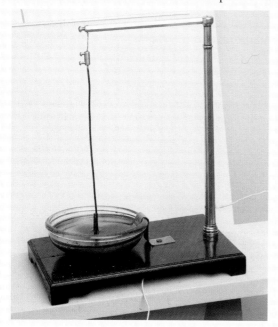

Figure 1.18   Faraday's apparatus demonstrating the principle of the electric motor. The upper end of a stiff wire is suspended in such a way that it is free to rotate. The lower end of the wire is immersed in the liquid metal mercury, and is free to move. The wire and its suspension form part of an electrical circuit that can be supplied with electric current from a battery. In the middle of the pool of mercury, next to the wire, is a short cylindrical magnet. When an electric current is passed through the wire it moves around the magnet. The use of mercury allows the current to continue flowing even though the wire is moving.

James Clerk Maxwell (1831–1879)

James Clerk Maxwell was the son of a Scottish laird. He studied at the Universities of Edinburgh and Cambridge and was appointed Professor of Natural Philosophy at Aberdeen at the age of 27. Four years later he moved to King's College, London, where he spent his most productive period. In 1865 he resigned his post in London but continued to work privately on his family estate in Scotland. In 1871 he agreed, somewhat reluctantly, to become the first Professor of Experimental Physics in the University of Cambridge. He died, from cancer, at the early age of 47, but by that time he had already made fundamental contributions to the theory of gases, the study of heat and thermodynamics, and, above all, to electromagnetism. He recast the discoveries of Faraday and others in mathematical form, added an important principle of his own and thus produced what are usually referred to as *Maxwell's equations* — the fundamental laws of electromagnetism (Figure 1.20). Much of his work on field theory was published in his masterpiece, *A Treatise on Electricity and Magnetism* (1873).

Figure 1.19   James Clerk Maxwell.

$$\mathrm{div}\, \mathbf{D} = \rho_f$$

$$\mathrm{div}\, \mathbf{B} = 0$$

$$\mathrm{curl}\, \mathbf{E} = -\frac{\partial \mathbf{B}}{\partial t}$$

$$\mathrm{curl}\, \mathbf{H} = \mathbf{j}_f + \frac{\partial \mathbf{D}}{\partial t}$$

Figure 1.20 Maxwell's equations, the fundamental laws of electromagnetism.

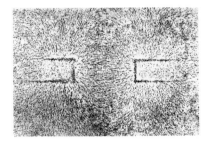

Figure 1.21 Magnetic field lines, as revealed by sprinkling iron filings onto a sheet of stiff paper placed on top of a magnet.

The problem that led Faraday to introduce the concept of a field was an old one; how could one body exert a force on another that was separated from it by empty space? Scientists and philosophers of earlier ages had devised essentially two possible answers.

- The simpler but less appealing possibility was that it just happened — that **action at a distance** was part of the fundamental reality of Nature and, as such, needed no further explanation.

- The other possibility was that the notion of empty space was a delusion, that the Universe was actually full of matter, albeit a very subtle and unusual form of matter, and that force was transmitted from one place to another by direct contact between parts of that matter. There were several different proposals concerning the exact nature of this 'subtle matter' that could transmit forces, but it was generally referred to as **ether**, and theories that made use of it were therefore called ether theories.

Newton's law of gravitation was taken to be an example of action at a distance. The law described the force that one body would exert on another some distance away without any regard to what was in between and without any hint of a mechanism for transmitting the force. Newton was aware that this was a feature of his 'System of the World' that many would find unattractive, but he also realized that he had no evidence on which to base a detailed explanation of gravitational forces. He contented himself with describing gravitational forces mathematically, and said in the *Principia*, that he would 'form no hypotheses' as to their cause.

Faraday, like others, was willing to accept this situation as far as a purely attractive force like gravity was concerned, or even for a force that could be attractive or repulsive like Coulomb's, but Faraday's own invention of the electric motor showed that the magnetic force on an electric current was not simply attractive or repulsive, it could cause rotation (see Figure 1.18). Faraday felt that for a wire to rotate around a magnet there had to be *something*, produced by the magnet but present at the location of the wire, that pushed the wire to one side rather than another. It was this agency, filling the space around the magnet, that Faraday eventually came to call a *magnetic field*.

Faraday's views about the nature of the magnetic field changed over time; for complex reasons, he spoke about his field as being different from an ether. Whatever his precise views, Faraday was convinced that fields held the key to understanding magnetic and electrical phenomena. He certainly felt that the curved pattern of lines revealed by sprinkling iron filings onto a sheet of paper placed over a magnet (see Figure 1.21) showed the presence of a magnetic field. Like a collection of miniature compass needles, the filings showed the field's strength and direction in each region of space. However, he also realized that in order to provide convincing evidence of the reality of the field something more was needed, such as a demonstration that a disturbance at one point in the field would take a finite time to propagate through the field and have visible effects elsewhere. Faraday tried to observe such delays, but failed. Nevertheless, his belief in the physical reality of fields guided his experiments and lead him on to new discoveries.

When Maxwell started to work on electromagnetism he studied Faraday's experimental researches and, unlike most of his contemporaries, was impressed by the notion of a field. However, Maxwell had his own reasons for believing in an ether. In particular, he believed that an ether was necessary to account for the propagation of light, which was generally regarded as a kind of wavelike disturbance and was therefore thought to *require* a medium just as ocean waves require water. Maxwell therefore decided to combine Faraday's field ideas with the ether concept. He set out to treat electricity and magnetism in terms of fields that were themselves interpreted as manifestations of pressure, tension and motion within the ether.

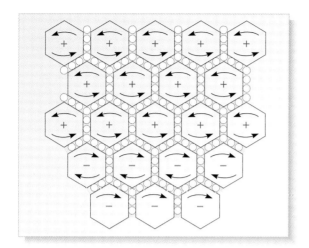

Figure 1.22   A part of Maxwell's mechanical model of the electromagnetic field. The model has been described as 'the most ingenious but least credible ever invented'.

In many ways, Maxwell was extraordinarily successful. He did formulate a mechanical model of the electromagnetic field (Figure 1.22) and used it as a guide in writing down his now famous equations. Amongst many other things, Maxwell's equations implied that light is a wave phenomenon in which electric and magnetic fields oscillate in space and time. In an astonishing demonstration of the power of these ideas, Maxwell took the fundamental constants of electricity and magnetism, entered them in his equations, and derived an accurate value for the speed of light. In this way, the subjects of electricity, magnetism and optics, which had seemed quite distinct at the beginning of the nineteenth century, were unified into a single branch of physics. The equations even led Maxwell to predict the existence of a wider family of electromagnetic waves, most with wavelengths beyond the range of human sight. In 1888 Heinrich Hertz completed a series of experiments which confirmed the existence of electromagnetic waves with wavelengths much greater than those of visible light. These were the radio waves which, within a few decades would transform both communication and entertainment. In 1895 Wilhelm Röntgen discovered X-rays, which proved to be electromagnetic waves with wavelengths much smaller than those of visible light. Yet, in spite of these successes, Maxwell's mechanical model of the electromagnetic field remained unconvincing. From about 1865, Maxwell himself drew a clear distinction between his equations, which described the behaviour of electric and magnetic fields, and the underlying ether mechanism that was supposed to account for them. Maxwell firmly believed that he had discovered the correct equations, but did not try to defend the model that had led to them.

If Maxwell had succeeded in accounting for the electromagnetic field in terms of motion in the ether, the mechanical world-view would have reigned supreme; but it was not to be. As investigations continued, particularly after Maxwell's untimely death, it became increasingly clear that it would be impossible to find a convincing mechanical basis for the electromagnetic field. On the other hand it also became clear that Maxwell's field theory of electromagnetism, as embodied in his equations, was stunningly successful.

Nowadays, with the scaffolding stripped away, we can recognize that the true achievement of Faraday and Maxwell was in establishing the importance of fields, arguably the most radical concept in physics since the time of Newton. We now know that there are many types of field: magnetic fields, electric fields, gravitational fields and so on. Each of these fields has a particular value at each point in space. The key idea is that a particle passing through a given point will experience forces that depend on the fields *at that point*, or in its immediate vicinity. This means that forces are determined locally — there is no action at a distance. When two particles interact they do so because one particle creates a field in the space around itself and the other particle then responds to this field. What is more, as Faraday anticipated and Maxwell's equations established, the fields have dynamics of their own, allowing disturbances of electric and magnetic fields to spread out as waves. Crucially, this means that fields should be thought of as *part of the fabric of the world* — more intangible than matter, but just as real. The electromagnetic field on Earth is incredibly complex. While you are reading this, electromagnetic waves from all the channels that your radio and television could possibly receive are passing straight through your head. Added to this are signals from power lines, domestic appliances, cars and the Big Bang; tiny electromagnetic signals are even reaching you from the brains of those around you. One of the attractions of physics is its ability to reveal a much richer world than is immediately apparent to our senses. And much stranger things are yet to come.

Question 1.4   Describe one way in which Maxwell's theory satisfied Faraday's desire to find evidence that disturbances at one point in the electromagnetic field would take a finite time to reach other points.   ■

4.2 Relativity, space, time and gravity

Throughout the development of mechanics and electromagnetism, the role of space and time had been clear and simple. Space and time were simply the arena within which the drama of physics was played out. Speaking metaphorically, the principal 'actors' were matter and ether/fields; space and time provided the setting but didn't get involved in the action. All that changed with the advent of the theory of relativity.

The theory was developed in two parts. The first part is called the special theory of relativity, or, occasionally, the restricted theory, and was introduced in 1905. The second part is called the general theory, and dates from about 1916. Both parts were devised by the same man, Albert Einstein.

The special theory of relativity is discussed in Book 6.

The origins of the **special theory of relativity** can be traced back a long way. In 1632, Galileo wrote:

> 'Shut yourself up with some friend in the main cabin below decks on some large ship, and have with you there some flies, butterflies and other small flying animals. Have a large bowl of water with some fish in it; hang up a bottle that empties drop by drop into a wide vessel beneath it. With the ship standing still, observe carefully how the little animals fly with equal speed to all sides of the cabin. The fish swim indifferently in all directions; the drop falls into the vessel beneath; and, in throwing something to your friend, you need throw no more strongly in one direction than another, the distances being equal; jumping with your feet together, you pass equal spaces in every direction. When you have observed all these things carefully (though there is no doubt that when the ship is standing still everything must happen in this way), have the ship proceed with any speed you like, so long as the motion is uniform and not fluctuating this way and that. You will discover not the least change in all the effects named, nor could you tell from any of them whether the ship was moving or standing still.'
>
>   Galileo Galilei (1632), *Dialogue Concerning the Two Chief Systems of the World.*

In other words, any phenomenon you care to study occurs in just the same way in a steadily moving ship as in a stationary ship. The underlying physical laws and fundamental constants must therefore be exactly the same for all uniformly moving (or stationary) observers. This fact, which dozing train passengers may accept with gratitude, is the central idea of the theory of special relativity. Indeed, it is called the **principle of relativity**. This leaves one obvious question: how did Einstein gain both fame and notoriety for promoting an idea that was nearly three hundred years old?

The answer is that a lot of physics had been discovered between the time of Galileo and that of Einstein. Most notably Maxwell's theory of electromagnetism had achieved the feat of *predicting* the speed of light using fundamental constants of electromagnetism, constants that could be measured using simple laboratory equipment such as batteries, coils and meters. Now, if the principle of relativity were extended to cover Maxwell's theory, the fundamental constants of electromagnetism would be the same for all uniformly moving observers and a very strange conclusion would follow: all uniformly moving observers would measure the *same* speed of light. Someone running towards a torch would measure the same speed of light as someone running away from the torch. Who would give credence to such a possibility?

Einstein had the courage, self-confidence and determination to reassert the principle of relativity and accept the consequences. He realized that, if the speed of light were to remain the same for all uniformly moving observers, space and time would have to have unexpected properties, leading to a number of startling conclusions, including the following:

- *Moving clocks run slow*. If I move steadily past you, you will find that my wrist watch is ticking *slower* than yours. Our biological clocks are also ticking, and you will also find that I am ageing less rapidly than you.

- *Moving rods contract*. If an observer on a platform measures the length of a passing railway carriage, he or she will measure a *shorter* length than that measured by a passenger who is sitting inside the carriage.

- *Simultaneity is relative*. Suppose you find two bells in different church towers striking at exactly the same time (i.e. simultaneously). If I move steadily past you, I will find that they strike at different times (i.e. not simultaneously). It is even possible for you to find that some event A happens before some other event B and for me to find that they occur in the *opposite* order.

- *The speed of light in a vacuum is a fundamental speed limit*. It is impossible to accelerate any material object up to this speed.

If these consequences seem absurd, please suspend your disbelief. It took the genius of Einstein to realize that there was nothing illogical or contradictory in these statements, but that they describe the world as it is. Admittedly we don't notice these effects in everyday life but that is because we move slowly: relativistic effects only become significant at speeds comparable with the speed of light (2.998×10^8 metres per second). But not everything moves slowly. The electrons in the tube of a TV set are one example, found in most homes, where relativistic effects are significant.

One of the first people to embrace Einstein's ideas was his former teacher, Hermann Minkowski (1864–1909). He realized that although different observers experience the same events, they will *describe* them differently because they disagree about the nature of space and the nature of time. On the other hand space and time taken together form a more robust entity:

> 'Henceforth space by itself, and time by itself, are doomed to fade away into mere shadows, and only a kind of union of the two will preserve an independent reality.'
>
> Hermann Minkowski, *Space and Time* in A. Einstein et al. (1952), *The Principle of Relativity*, New York, Dover Publications.

The union of space and time of which Minkowski spoke is now generally referred to as *space-time*. It represents a kind of melding together of space and time, and since space is three-dimensional, and time is one-dimensional, space-time is four-dimensional. Any particular observer, such as you or I, will divide space-time into space and time, but the way in which that division is made may differ from one observer to another and will crucially depend on the relative motion of the observers.

A very rough attempt at representing diagrammatically this change of attitude towards space and time is shown in Figure 1.23. Before Einstein introduced special relativity, the phrase 'the whole of space at a particular time' was thought to have exactly the same meaning for all observers. After Einstein's work it was felt that each observer would understand what the phrase meant, but that different observers would *disagree* about what constituted the whole of space at a particular time. All observers would agree on what constituted space-time, but the way in which it was sliced up into space and time would differ from one observer to another, depending on their relative motion. No observer had the true view; they were all equally valid even though they might be different.

In retrospect, special relativity can be seen as part of a gradual process in which the laws of physics attained universal significance. The earliest attempts to understand the physical world placed Man and the Earth firmly at the centre of creation. Certain laws applied on Earth, but different laws applied in the heavens. Copernicus overturned this Earth-centred view and Newton proposed laws that claimed to apply at all places, and at all times. Special relativity continues this process by insisting that physical laws should not depend on the observer's state of motion — at least so long as that motion is uniform. It is therefore not surprising that Einstein was led to ask if physical laws could be expressed in the same way for *all* observers, even those who were moving *non-uniformly*. This was the aim of his **general theory of relativity**.

Einstein realized that many of the effects of non-uniform motion are similar to the effects of gravity. (Perhaps you have experienced the sensation of feeling heavier in a lift that is accelerating upwards.) With unerring instinct he treated this as a vital clue: any theory of general relativity would also have to be a theory of gravity. After more than ten years of struggle, the new theory was ready. According to general relativity, a large concentration of mass, such as the Earth, significantly distorts space-time in its vicinity. Bodies moving through a region of distorted space-time move differently from the way they would have moved in an undistorted space-time.

Figure 1.23 (a) The pre-Einsteinian view of space and time. Not only are space and time separate and distinct they are also absolute. All observers agree on what constitutes space and what constitutes time, and they also agree about what it means to speak of 'the whole of space at a particular time'. (b) The post-Einsteinian view in which space and time are seen as aspects of a unified space-time. Different observers in uniform, relative motion will each slice space-time into space and time, but they will do so in different ways. Each observer knows what it means to speak of 'the whole of space at a particular time', but different observers no longer necessarily agree about what constitutes space and what constitutes time.

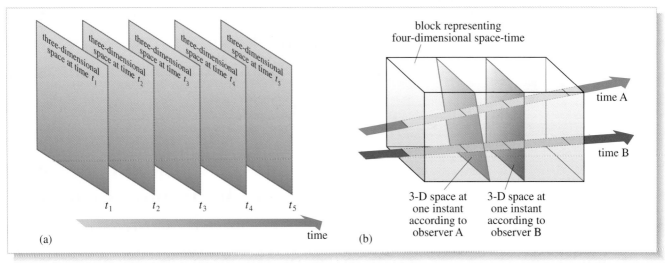

For example, meteors coming close to the Earth are attracted to it and deviate from uniform, steady motion in a straight line. Newton would have had no hesitation in saying that these deviations are due to gravitational forces. In Einstein's view, however, *there is no force*. The meteors move in the simplest way imaginable, but through a distorted space-time, and it is this distortion, generated by the presence of the Earth, that provides the attraction. This is the essence of general relativity, though the mathematics required to spell it out properly is quite formidable, even for a physicist.

The central ideas of general relativity have been neatly summarized by the American physicist John Archibald Wheeler. In a now famous phrase Wheeler said:

'Matter tells space how to curve.

Space tells matter how to move.'

Purists might quibble over whether Wheeler should have said 'space-time' rather than 'space', but as a two-line summary of general relativity this is hard to beat (see Figure 1.24). If you tried to summarize Newtonian gravitation in the same way all you could say is: 'Matter tells matter how to move'; the contrast is clear.

General relativity is a field theory of gravity. At its heart are a set of equations called the Einstein field equations. To this extent general relativity is similar to Maxwell's field theory of electromagnetism. But general relativity is a very unusual field theory. Whereas electric and magnetic fields exist *in* space and time, the gravitational field essentially *is* space and time. Einstein was well aware of the contrast between gravity and electromagnetism, and spent a good deal of the later part of his life trying to formulate a **unified field theory** in which gravity and electromagnetism would be combined into a single 'geometric' field theory. In this quest he was ultimately unsuccessful, but general relativity remains a monumental achievement.

> You should leave the text at this point and view Video 1: *A Life of Time*. When you have viewed the video you should return to this text.

Question 1.5   Would it be fair to say that special relativity has the effect of leaving each observer completely free to make his or her own decision about what constitutes time? ■

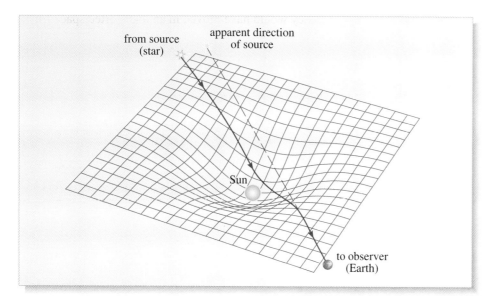

Figure 1.24   A highly schematic diagram showing space-time curvature near the Sun and indicating the way in which this can lead to the bending of starlight as it grazes the edge of the Sun. (The bending has been hugely exaggerated for the sake of clarity.) The observation of this effect in 1919, during a total eclipse of the Sun, did much to make Einstein an international celebrity.

Albert Einstein (1879–1955)

Figure 1.25 Albert Einstein.

Albert Einstein was born in Ulm, Germany on 14 March 1879. The following year he and his family moved to Munich where he had a successful, though not brilliant, school career. In 1896 Einstein renounced his German citizenship and started to study for a high-school teaching diploma at the prestigious Eidgenössische Technische Hochschule (ETH) in Zurich, Switzerland. Amongst his fellow students at ETH was Mileva Maric, who became his first wife. Einstein graduated in 1900 and in December of that year submitted his first paper to a scientific journal. However, he failed to get any of the university positions that he applied for, and after some temporary school teaching he became, in 1902, a technical expert (third-class) at the patent office in Bern. He continued to pursue his interest in physics while at the patent office, and worked on a doctoral thesis during his spare time.

1905 was an extraordinary year in Einstein's life and in the progress of science. During that year he produced four of his most important papers. In the first he explained Brownian motion — the apparently random motion exhibited by pollen grains and other small particles when they are suspended in a fluid. According to Einstein, the motion is a result of the incessant bombardment of the suspended particles by molecules of the fluid. The quantitative success of this explanation established beyond reasonable doubt the existence of molecules, which until then had been questioned by many physicists. In his second 1905 paper, Einstein formulated a theory of the

photoelectric effect — the liberation of electrons from a metal exposed to electromagnetic radiation. His explanation was one of the earliest applications of quantum physics and was an important step in the development of that subject. It was mainly for this piece of work that Einstein was awarded the Nobel Prize for Physics in 1921. His third and fourth 1905 papers concerned the special theory of relativity. He laid out the foundations of the subject in the third paper and in the fourth he provided a brief but eloquent justification of his famous equation $E = mc^2$, which uses c, the speed of light in a vacuum, to relate the mass m of a body to its total energy content E.

> ## ON THE ELECTRODYNAMICS OF MOVING BODIES
>
> BY
>
> **A. EINSTEIN**
>
> *Translated from "Zur Elektrodynamik bewegter Körper,"*
> *Annalen der Physik, 17, 1905.*

Figure 1.26 Einstein's 1905 paper *On the Electrodynamics of Moving Bodies*. This was his first paper on special relativity.

Although these brilliantly original papers eventually established Einstein as a physicist of the first rank, three more years were to elapse before he obtained his first academic post. During that time he worked on a variety of topics and did pioneering work on the quantum physics of solids. In 1909 he was finally appointed to a lecturing post at the University of Bern, in 1911 he became a professor at the University of Prague and in 1912 he returned to Zurich, as Professor of Theoretical Physics at ETH. By this time his attention was focused on the search for a general theory of relativity that would extend his earlier work on the special theory. The principle of equivalence which he formulated in 1907 had convinced Einstein that a general theory of relativity would also be a new theory of gravity, and it was from the gravitational point of view that the problem of general relativity was attacked. In 1914 Einstein moved to Berlin, the main centre of scientific research in the German-speaking world, to take up a research professorship that would free him from teaching duties. He and his wife separated soon after the move, and were eventually divorced. Einstein continued to work on general relativity and in 1916 produced the first systematic treatment of the subject in a long paper entitled *Die Grundlage der allgemeinen Relativätstheorie* ('The foundations of general relativity theory'). The creation of general relativity was one of the greatest intellectual achievements of the twentieth century: it led on to the study of black holes and the prediction of gravitational waves, and it provided a firm basis for future investigations in cosmology — the study of the Universe as a whole. Observations carried out in 1919, during a total eclipse of the Sun, confirmed one of the key predictions of general relativity: the gravitational deflection of starlight passing close to the edge of the Sun. This quantitative success of Einstein's theory was widely reported, and did more than any other event to make Einstein into an instantly recognized icon of scientific genius.

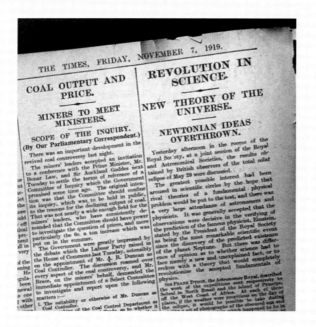

Figure 1.27   The article from the Times of November 7, 1919. Copyright Times Newspapers Limited, 1919.

Soon after completing the general theory, Einstein turned his attention to the quantum theory of electromagnetic radiation and postulated the existence of stimulated emission — the process that now underpins the operation of lasers. However, in 1917 he became seriously ill. He was nursed back to health by his cousin Elsa, whom he married in 1919. His second marriage seems to have been reasonably happy, but he was not, by his own admission, a good husband.

By the early 1920s Einstein's best scientific work was done: he wrote in 1921 'Discovery in the grand manner is for young people… and hence for me is a thing of the past'. He was none the less extremely influential in the physics community and he did much to prepare the ground for many later developments. He travelled a lot, and became increasingly active in social and political causes, particularly in support of Zionism. (Many years later he was offered the presidency of Israel, which he declined.) In 1932, Einstein and his wife left Germany for good, mainly in response to growing anti-Semitism, and moved to the USA where Einstein settled as a professor at the Institute for Advanced Study in Princeton, New Jersey. Einstein eventually became an American citizen, though he also retained the Swiss citizenship he had held since his twenties. Although Einstein was a believer in peace and harmony, and eventually argued for a world government, he also recognized the dangers of Nazism and the potential power of atomic science. As a result, in 1939, he was persuaded to co-sign a letter to the American President, Franklin D. Roosevelt, warning of the possibility of atomic weapons. This is widely thought to have had a decisive effect in prompting the US government to undertake the development of the atomic bomb, though Einstein himself played no part in the project.

Although Einstein had been deeply involved in the birth of quantum physics, he became increasingly dissatisfied with the way the subject developed after the mid-1920s. He did not believe that it gave a truly fundamental account of natural phenomena. His last major contribution to the field was the development of Bose–Einstein statistics in 1925. However his name is also recalled in the Einstein–Podolsky–Rosen experiment, a 'thought experiment' proposed in 1935 in an attempt to show that quantum physics was seriously flawed. The attempt was unconvincing, but it did emphasize the gulf that separated quantum physics from the classical physics that preceded it. The other project of Einstein's later years that continues to be remembered is his search for a unified field theory that would bring together gravity and electromagnetism. He continued to work on this up to the time of his death, often with great ingenuity, but little of that work is regarded as being of enduring value. He died in Princeton in 1955.

5 The uncertain Universe

Despite the impact of relativity, the greatest source of change in the scientific world-view in the twentieth century has undoubtedly been the development of *quantum physics*. This is the branch of physics that is mainly concerned with microscopic entities such as atoms and molecules, and their constituents. It is by far the most quantitatively accurate part of science, routinely providing predictions that are correct to just a few parts in a million. Quantum physics is also of enormous technological importance since it provides the scientific underpinning for the modern electronics industry which brings us devices ranging from TV sets and transistor radios to CD players and computers.

So great has been its effect that it is now conventional to divide physics into two parts; **quantum physics** and **classical physics**, where, by classical physics, we mean anything that is not quantum physics. To be fair, it should be noted that some authors prefer to define classical physics as consisting of those subjects that were already well-defined by the year 1900, together with their direct developments in the twentieth century. In this way they include mechanics, thermodynamics and electromagnetism, but they exclude special and general relativity. Most physicists, however, would not hesitate to say that general relativity was a classical theory of gravity, and would regard relativity as the culmination of classical physics rather than a step beyond it. In any event, there can be no doubt that the development of quantum physics has demanded a fundamental change in outlook by physicists.

Quantum physics was born in 1900, but it took about twenty five years to reach maturity. During the first quarter of the twentieth century it had a rather rickety feel; there was not really any coherent theory of quantum physics, just assorted quantum ideas that were so successful in solving certain outstanding puzzles that it seemed there had to be something behind it all. The strongest characteristic of quantum physics during this early period was an emphasis on graininess or discreteness.

Indeed, the word *quantum* actually comes from the Latin for 'unit of quantity' or 'amount' and was introduced into physics by the German scientist Max Planck (1858–1947), in the course of his investigations into the emission of electromagnetic radiation from hot surfaces.

Crudely speaking, Planck was looking into why hot things glow. He knew that the light given off by a heated object is a mixture of all the possible colours of light and he wanted to predict the relative brightness with which each colour would be emitted

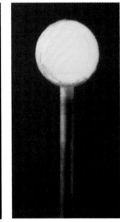

Figure 1.28 The changing colour of a heated body. The emitted light is a mixture of colours. As the temperature rises the relative brightness of each of the constituent colours changes.

from an object at a given temperature. It was changes in these relative brightnesses as temperature increased that explained why objects went from being red-hot at fairly low temperatures to white-hot or blue-hot at fairly high temperatures (Figure 1.28).

Planck found that, in order to account for the observed pattern of emission from hot bodies, he had to assume that energy was transferred from the heated surface to the emitted radiation in a 'grainy' way. Corresponding to each particular colour of light there was a minimum amount of energy — a *quantum* of energy — that could be carried away from the surface by the light. The size of this quantum of energy depended on the colour of the light; an energy quantum of violet light was almost twice as energetic as an energy quantum of red light, and every other colour had its own characteristic quantum. Planck was able to write down a law that related the quantum of energy corresponding to any particular colour to the physical property (frequency) which determined that colour. In doing so he introduced a new fundamental constant of Nature — now called **Planck's constant** ($h = 6.626 \times 10^{-34}$ joule seconds). The appearance of Planck's constant in a calculation can be taken as a clear indication that quantum physics is involved.

Planck's law was used with great success over the following quarter of a century, in a variety of contexts. Einstein used it in his 1905 paper explaining the photoelectric effect, and so did the Danish physicist Niels Bohr (1885–1962), in 1913, when he formulated a theory of the inner workings of the atom that achieved some remarkable successes in spite of a number of unsatisfactory features. It showed up again in 1924 in the doctoral thesis of Louis de Broglie (1892–1987), who suggested that entities which are normally thought of as particles, such as electrons, actually have a wave-like aspect to their behaviour. Einstein, Bohr and de Broglie all received Nobel Prizes in recognition of their work.

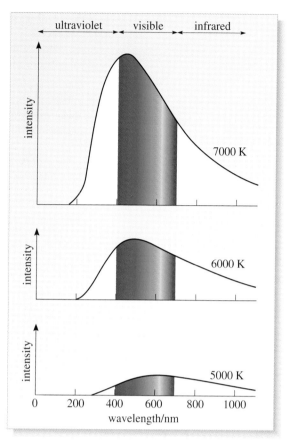

Figure 1.29 Graphs showing the relative intensity of each colour in the light emitted by ideal emitters at different temperatures.

These early developments were strikingly out of step with conventional classical physics. They might even be described as revolutionary, but the real revolution was still to come.

5.1 Quantum mechanics and chance

The real quantum revolution dates from the formulation of **quantum mechanics** by Werner Heisenberg (1901–1976) and others in 1925, and its physical interpretation by Max Born (1882–1970) in 1926. However, before attempting even the most basic sketch of quantum mechanics let's take a small diversion into the realm of philosophy.

The principles of quantum mechanics are discussed in Book 7 and some of its applications are described in Book 8.

The basic working philosophy of most scientists, including those who say they have no philosophy, is a kind of **realism**. (Philosophers recognize many shades of realism.) The three main points of this creed are:

● Our senses allow us to observe a physical world, and our bodies allow us to interact with that world.

● Although our perceptions may differ, we all share the same physical world, which exists independently of our observations, e.g. the same Moon is really out there for all of us, even if none of us is looking at it.

● Although our actions may cause disturbances, it is possible to investigate the physical world without destroying its essential structure. We may therefore try to deduce the essential features of the physical world by combining experiment and observation with rational speculation.

One of the many astonishing features of quantum mechanics is that it calls into question some of the central ideas of this kind of realist philosophy. When speaking about the nature of the microscopic entities that are described by quantum mechanics one of the subject's pioneers said:

'…they form a world of potentialities or possibilities rather than one of things or facts.'

Werner Heisenberg

Another of the quantum pioneers put it even more simply:

'There is no quantum world.'

Niels Bohr

Let's see how such statements came to be made.

By 1925 it was clear that atoms consisted of positively charged cores, called *nuclei*, around which swarmed negatively charged *electrons*. It was also clear that conventional classical mechanics was incapable of correctly describing the behaviour of those electrons, and the search was on for a new mechanics that could be applied to particles in the atomic domain. The (limited) success of Bohr's model of the atom indicated that the new mechanics would involve Planck's constant, so Max Born, a leading atomic researcher at the University of Göttingen in Germany, named the new mechanics *quantum mechanics*, even though he had no real idea of its basic rules at the time. It was supposed that quantum mechanics would be more fundamental than classical mechanics, so that once the rules of quantum mechanics were uncovered it would be possible to deduce the laws of classical mechanics from them.

Those basic rules of quantum mechanics were actually brought to light over a period of about a year, starting in the summer of 1925. The first breakthrough was made by Werner Heisenberg, a 24-year-old researcher at Göttingen, who had been working closely with Born. Heisenberg's first paper on the subject sketched out his basic ideas, but it was far from being a systematic formulation of quantum mechanics; neither the mathematical basis of quantum mechanics (its *formalism*) nor its physical meaning (its *interpretation*) was at all clear. Intensive work by Heisenberg, Born and others over the next six months did much to clarify the formalism (which turned out to involve mathematical objects called *matrices*), and to show that quantum mechanics was at least as successful as Bohr's rather unsatisfactory atomic theory, but it did not clarify the interpretation. At that stage, early in 1926, Erwin Schrödinger (1887–1961), an Austrian working at the University of Zurich, published a different and somewhat simpler formulation of quantum mechanics. Schrödinger's approach was based on de Broglie's idea that matter has a wave-like aspect. Schrödinger himself soon showed that his approach was mathematically equivalent to that of Heisenberg, but he too had difficulty working out what it all meant.

The key step in the interpretation of quantum mechanics was first put into print by Born in June 1926. Imagine that you could arrange a collision between a particle and a target and that, after the collision, the particle was deflected to the left. If you could repeat the collision under *exactly* the same conditions, you would naturally expect to see the particle deflected to the left again. If the particle were unexpectedly deflected to the right you would probably assume that the second collision had been set up in a slightly different way to the first, in spite of your best efforts to make the conditions identical. Born used the new formalism of quantum mechanics to study collisions and realized that, in utter contrast to classical expectations, *quantum mechanics allows identical experiments to have different outcomes*. Two collisions could be set up in *exactly* the same way (the discreteness of quantum mechanics helps to enable this). Yet, in spite of starting out in the same way, a particle may be deflected to the left in one collision and to the right in the other. In any single collision it is impossible to predict which way the particle will go.

You might wonder whether science is possible at all if Nature behaves so capriciously. Fortunately, quantum mechanics does allow us to make predictions, but with some uncertainty. In any experiment, the formalism of quantum mechanics can, in principle, predict:

- the possible outcomes;
- the **probability** (i.e. the relative likelihood or chance) of each of those possible outcomes.

However, what quantum mechanics cannot do, and what Born was convinced it would never do, was to go beyond probabilities and predict a definite outcome for a particular experiment that might have more than one outcome. Returning to the example of collisions, quantum mechanics can predict that particles colliding in a certain way might be deflected to the left *or* to the right; it can also predict the *probability* of deflection to the left or the right and hence the relative numbers deflected left or right in a large number of identical collisions; but it cannot predict whether a particular particle in a particular collision will be deflected right or left. Dealing with probabilities is an *intrinsic* part of quantum physics that cannot be avoided.

The use of probability in physics was not new. But the suggestion that probability was intrinsic and unavoidable was shocking. In classical physics, probability was used when something which could be known in principle (such as the exact path of a particle) was not known; probability filled the gap left by ignorance. Statistical mechanics, for example, used probabilities to estimate likely pressures and entropies, compensating for ignorance about detailed molecular motions. It was not doubted however, that such details existed, and could be determined in principle. In quantum mechanics the situation was completely different; a probabilistic statement along the lines of 'this has a 30% chance of happening' might well be the *most* that could be said in a certain situation, even in principle.

Niels Bohr, whose atomic theory was overthrown by quantum mechanics, was a keen supporter of the new mechanics. He had partly inspired Heisenberg to undertake its development in the first place, and in May 1926 he welcomed Heisenberg to his institute in Copenhagen where a great deal of effort went into formulating a complete interpretation of quantum mechanics that included the idea of intrinsic probabilities. The **Copenhagen interpretation** that emerged from this work is now regarded as the conventional interpretation of quantum mechanics, though there have always been those who have questioned its correctness. Some of the features of this interpretation are:

- The measurable properties of objects (position, velocity, etc.) do not generally have values except just after a measurement.
- Measurement causes potentiality to become actuality.
- The measured values occur at frequencies determined by probabilistic rules. The probabilities are intrinsic and fundamental, and can be predicted by quantum mechanics.

The last of these points represents a substantial shift from classical determinism. In classical mechanics the past uniquely determines the present and hence the future. In

Figure 1.30 A quantum mechanical model of a hydrogen atom, which has *one* electron, in its state of lowest energy. The varying density of the spots indicates the relative likelihood of finding the electron in any particular region.

quantum mechanics this is not so. Even the most complete possible knowledge of the past would only permit the calculation of the probability of future events. Some, perhaps a little naively, saw in this a scientific basis for free will: there was an element of freedom, or at least of chance, in the Universe.

The Copenhagen interpretation calls simple realism into question. If the most that you can say about a position measurement you are about to perform is that various values may be obtained, with various probabilities, then it may well mean that the object has no position until it is measured. Note that this is quite different from saying that the object has a position which you don't happen to know — it is as if the object had not made up its mind where to appear until the position measurement has been made. Clearly if you say that the object has *no* position, you call into question its independent reality, and hence the philosophy of realism, at least in its simplest form. This emphasizes the enormous importance of measurement in quantum physics and the motivation for making statements such as '… they form a world of potentialities or possibilities rather than one of things or facts' and 'there is no quantum world'.

An alternative stance is to assume that there is a real world out there, but to admit that it cannot be adequately described in terms of classical concepts such as position or velocity. This is plausible. We have no right to expect microscopic physics to be just a scaled-down version of everyday experience. Given that quantum mechanics deals with a microscopic world well beyond the immediate reach of our senses and intuitions, perhaps the most surprising thing is that we can make predictions at all. From this perspective, the price that must be paid for the mismatch between our classical concepts and the quantum world is astonishingly small, and is reflected mainly in the appearance of probabilities. In philosophical terms, the concept of a real world can be preserved by admitting that certain aspects of it are inaccessible to us, clumsy giants that we are. But in practical, or scientific, terms this makes no difference. It is hard to see how we could ever develop an understanding that was not based on classical concepts, so probabilities seem destined to remain intrinsic and unavoidable, offering the only gateway through which we can glimpse the microscopic world.

Question 1.6   In Section 1 it was said that the notion of scientific law was based on the fact that identical situations produced identical outcomes. To what extent does this remain true in quantum physics where identical experiments may produce different outcomes?   ■

5.2 Quantum fields and unification

From its inception, quantum physics was concerned not just with particles such as electrons, but also with light and other forms of electromagnetic radiation. In 1900 Planck discovered the quantum in the transfer of energy from matter to radiation, and in 1905, Einstein's explanation of the photoelectric effect assumed that the transfer of energy from radiation to matter occurred in a similarly quantized fashion. It is therefore hardly surprising that the development of quantum mechanics was soon followed by an attempt to formulate a quantum theory of electromagnetic radiation. That meant, of course, combining quantum ideas such as Planck's constant and intrinsic probabilities with the field theory of electromagnetism. The result would be a **quantum field theory**.

The quantum field theory of electromagnetism is called **quantum electrodynamics**, or QED for short. Its formulation proved to be very difficult. The first steps were taken by the British physicist Paul Dirac in 1927, but the theory was not really sorted out until the late 1940s.

Paul Adrien Maurice Dirac (1902–1984)

Paul Adrien Maurice Dirac was born in Bristol, England, in 1902. His father was a Swiss-born teacher of French, his mother a librarian. Dirac's first degree, obtained at the Merchant Venturer's Technical College, was in electrical engineering, but he had no real interest in the subject and after graduating spent two years studying mathematics at the University of Bristol. In 1923 he left Bristol for Cambridge where he remained for most of his working life.

Dirac's achievements in Cambridge were prodigious. In 1925, while working for his doctorate, he became one of the founders of quantum mechanics when he produced an elegant extension of Heisenberg's work. A little over a year later he presented a very general formulation of quantum mechanics that has remained the basis of the subject ever since. During the next year he essentially founded quantum electrodynamics. In 1928 Dirac took an important step towards bringing quantum physics into conformity with Einstein's special theory of relativity by devising an equation (now called the Dirac equation) that could describe the behaviour of electrons at any speed up to the speed of light. This equation provided a natural explanation of one of the electron's intrinsic properties — its spin. Taking the mathematical form of his equation seriously, and searching for a way of interpreting it, Dirac was led, in 1931, to propose that there should exist a class of 'anti-electrons', particles with the same mass and spin as the electron but with the opposite electrical charge (Figure 1.32). By correctly predicting the existence of these antiparticles, now called positrons, Dirac became recognized as the 'discoverer' of antimatter — one of the most important discoveries of the century.

From 1932 to 1969 Dirac held the Lucasian Chair of Mathematics in Cambridge, the post that Newton himself had once occupied. During this period Dirac

Figure 1.31   Paul Dirac.

worked on a variety of topics including *magnetic monopoles* (hypothetical magnetic charges) and the speculation that the fundamental constants of physics might be gradually changing in a co-ordinated way. However he became disenchanted with some of the detailed developments that occurred in quantum field theory and became increasingly distanced from what others regarded as the scientific mainstream.

In 1971, following his retirement from Cambridge, Dirac moved to the USA where he became a professor of physics at Florida State University. He died there in 1984. Throughout his life Dirac was renowned for his economy of speech and lack of social awareness. His book *Principles of Quantum Mechanics* (1930) is regarded as a classic of clear and elegant exposition. When a correspondent asked him to clarify a certain result in the text, Dirac is said to have replied that he knew of no clearer way of expressing the point. No rudeness would have been intended, just an honest statement of fact. Dirac preferred to work by himself, and had few collaborators or research students.

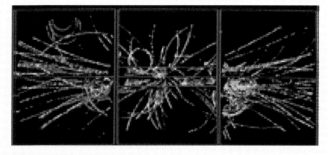

Figure 1.32   Tracks left by fundamental particles. (a) An electron and a positron (a particle–antiparticle pair) reveal their opposite charges by spiralling in different directions in a magnetic field. (b) A variety of particles created from the energy released when an electron and a positron collide at high speed and annihilate.

During the lengthy development of QED the following important features of quantum field theory became apparent.

- *Quantum field theory provides the natural way of combining special relativity and quantum physics.* Quantum mechanics, as originally formulated by Heisenberg and Schrödinger was inconsistent with the principle of relativity. Attempts were made to rectify this problem and significant progress was made by Dirac with his relativistic electron equation. However, despite many successes it became increasingly clear that relativistic quantum mechanics was ultimately self-contradictory and that quantum field theory provided the natural way of producing a relativistic quantum physics.

- *Quantum fields may be regarded as collections of particles.* In the case of the quantized electromagnetic field these particles are called **photons**. Each photon of a particular colour carries a characteristic amount of energy: the quantum of energy used by Planck and Einstein. Emission and absorption of radiation corresponds to the creation and destruction of photons and therefore inevitably involves the transfer of complete quanta of energy. (Interestingly, Einstein realized as early as 1905 that the quantized transfer of energy would be explained if radiation actually consisted of particles, but the idea was not well received and he did not press it. Photons only became an accepted part of physics in the 1920s.)

- *Quantum field theory can be used to describe all fundamental particles.* Electrons and positrons are normally regarded as examples of fundamental particles of matter. In quantum field theory all such particles are associated with quantum fields in much the same way that photons are associated with the electromagnetic field. The number of particles of a given type reflects the state of excitation of the field, and the particles are said to be 'quanta of excitation' of the field. Thus, although quantum field theory describes particles and the forces between them, it does so entirely in terms of quantum fields.

- *Quantum field theory describes processes in which particles are created or destroyed.* When a quantum field becomes more excited, the number of quanta of excitation increases. This occurs because new particle–antiparticle pairs are created from radiation. When a quantum field becomes less excited, the number of quanta of excitation decreases. This is achieved by processes in which particles and antiparticles collide and annihilate one another to produce radiation. (Both of these processes are permitted by Einstein's $E = mc^2$, and were explicitly predicted by Dirac.)

These were all very attractive features of quantum field theory and raised the hope that it might be a truly fundamental theory capable of providing a new world-view. However there were serious problems within quantum electrodynamics that had to be overcome before such hopes stood any chance of being realized. Using QED to predict the value of a physically measurable quantity involved, in practice, working out the contribution made by several different sub-processes. Making sure that these sub-processes were fully identified was a problem in itself, working out their individual contributions was even worse. Even in the simplest cases determining the contributions was difficult, and in the more complicated cases the result was usually a meaningless infinity showing that something was wrong. It was the problem of infinities that really delayed the completion of QED until the late 1940s. At that time, in a burst of post-war activity, a technique called *renormalization* was developed that made it possible to get at the physical result hidden behind the unphysical infinity. At the same time a simple diagrammatic method was devised that made it much easier to identify and perform the necessary calculations. The problem of infinities was solved by Julian Schwinger (1918–1994), Sin-itiro Tomonaga (1906–1979) and Richard P. Feynman. The last of these was also responsible for the diagrams, which have become known as *Feynman diagrams* (Figure 1.33).

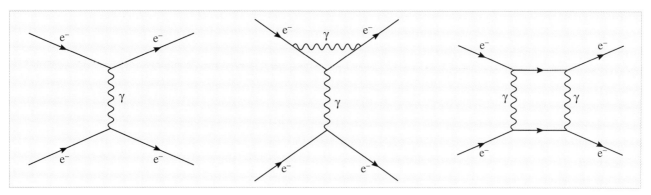

Figure 1.33   Feynman diagrams of some of the processes that contribute to the scattering of colliding electrons. Each diagram represents a complicated mathematical expression. The wavy lines represent photons.

Richard P. Feynman (1918–1988)

Figure 1.34   Richard P. Feynman.

Richard Phillips Feynman was one of the most colourful and celebrated of US physicists. He was born in New York in 1918 and educated at the Massachusetts Institute of Technology (MIT) and Princeton. From 1942 to 1945 he was involved in the atomic bomb project at Los Alamos, where he gave ample evidence of his enormous technical virtuosity as well as earning himself a reputation as a practical joker.

After the Second World War Feynman went to Cornell University where he became one of the major figures in the development of quantum electrodynamics (QED). During this period he also devised his own approach to quantum mechanics called the 'path integral' or 'sum over histories' approach. This has since been applied to quantum field theory and is now the standard formalism in many areas of the subject.

In 1950 Feynman moved to the California Institute of Technology (Caltech) where he remained for the rest of his life. While there, he worked on many topics, including the theory of fundamental particles, the theory of superfluidity and the nature of the forces and interactions within the atomic nucleus. He became renowned as a teacher of physics, combining profound physical insight with a very down-to-earth style. Towards the end of his life, when already ill with cancer, he was invited to join the commission investigating the in-flight explosion of the space shuttle *Challenger*. As part of that work he memorably demonstrated, in front of a massive TV audience, the disastrous effect of low temperature on the booster rocket's O-ring seals by dropping one of them into a glass of iced water.

Feynman will long be remembered as one of the twentieth century's greatest exponents of intuitive — yet highly rigorous — physics. The three volumes of *Feynman Lectures on Physics* from his Caltech years, and Feynman's autobiographical works '*Surely You're Joking Mr Feynman!*' and '*What Do You Care What Other People Think?*' also ensure that he will be remembered as a character of extraordinary insight, wit and charm. In 1965 Feynman shared the Nobel Prize for Physics with Julian Schwinger and Sin-itiro Tomonaga.

The completion of QED presented physicists with the most precise theory of Nature they had ever possessed. However, by the time that completion had been achieved it was already clear that electromagnetism and gravitation were not the only forces at work in the world. The familiar contact forces you feel when pressing on a surface had long been understood to be nothing more than manifestations of electromagnetism — atoms repelling other atoms that got too close — but the 1930s and 1940s had provided clear evidence of the existence of two other fundamental forces. These new forces were quite powerful, but both were of such short range that they mainly operated within atoms rather than between them. The new forces were called the **strong** and **weak nuclear forces** since their effects were most clearly seen in the behaviour of atomic nuclei. The major properties of all four of the fundamental forces are listed in Table 1.1.

Table 1.1 The four fundamental forces. The strengths are roughly those found at high collision energies, and the force carriers are the particles most closely associated with each force. The graviton is followed by a question mark because its existence is still in doubt.

Force	Strength	Range	Force carrier
strong	10^{-1}	10^{-15} m	gluon
electromagnetic	10^{-2}	infinite	photon
weak	10^{-2}	10^{-17} m	W and Z bosons
gravitational	10^{-45}	infinite	graviton(?)

Formulating quantum field theories of each of the four fundamental forces was an obvious goal, and remains so to this day. Three of the forces — the strong, the weak and the electromagnetic — have been treated with great success; and have been combined to form a so-called *standard model* of fundamental forces. However, gravity has resisted all attempts to fit it into the same kind of theoretical strait-jacket and seems to require very special treatment if it is to be treated as a quantum field theory at all. If it were not for the problem of gravity we would be able to say that the physicist's current world-view is that the Universe consists of a set of mutually interacting quantum fields that fill the space-time described by special relativity. But it seems that this will not do.

A way forward may be indicated by the standard model itself. The standard model is actually something more than a description of three of the four fundamental forces; it is also to some extent a prototype for their union. Within the standard model the electromagnetic and weak forces appear as a unified electroweak force. The exact meaning of **unification** in this context is too technical to go into here, but suffice it to say that, under unification, the quantum fields responsible for the weak and electromagnetic forces combine in a way that is slightly reminiscent of Einstein's fusion of space and time to form space-time.

The success of electroweak unification has been one of the motivations for suggesting that all three of the forces that appear in the standard model might be unified within a grand unified theory, and that a further step of unification might also incorporate gravity, thus bringing all four fundamental forces within a single *superunified* theory. The form that such a superunified theory might take is far from clear. Would it involve quantum fields in a curved space-time, or would something altogether more radical be required?

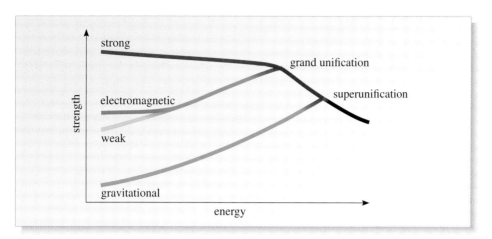

Figure 1.35 A possible route to superunification of the four fundamental forces. At low energies we have laboratory evidence of four forces, but the weak and electromagnetic forces are known to acquire a common strength at high energies. Perhaps this process continues.

For some time many hoped that an approach called *string theory* might provide a solution to the problem of superunification. The idea of this approach was that the basic entities were not quantized fields that filled the points of four-dimensional space-time, but rather extended objects called *strings* that vibrated in ten or more dimensions. There was never any experimental evidence to support this idea, but what really caused theorists to lose faith in it was the discovery that string theory is not unique. There is a strong prejudice amongst those searching for a unified theory of everything that there should only be one such theory, not a whole class of them. String theory fails to satisfy this uniqueness criterion. However, hope of string-based superunification has not been entirely lost. A new subject called *M-theory* is being investigated in which all of the plausible string theories appear as different aspects of a single theory — perhaps.

At the present time, the quest to find the ultimate constituents of the Universe and the laws that regulate their behaviour ends not with an answer, but with a set of loose ends. Perhaps this is as it should be in a healthy science, or perhaps it is a sign that we are heading towards a dead end. Perhaps there is no single world-view for physics to uncover, or perhaps it is not the function of physics to do so.

Question 1.7   Does quantum field theory suffer from the same kind of conflict with simple realism that arose in quantum mechanics?   ■

5.3 The end of physics?

Suppose for the moment that quantum field theory, or string theory or M-theory, or some other theory no one has yet heard of, does turn out to be the much sought-after superunified theory. Suppose it is unique and is so wonderfully compact that it can be printed on the front of a teeshirt. What would such a theory really tell us about the world?

Looking on the positive side, the theory should indicate the fundamental entities of which the world is composed, whether they are particles, strings, quantum fields, or whatever. The theory should also indicate the truly fundamental constants of Nature (it may be that Planck's constant, the speed of light and so on are not really as fundamental as we think), and it should certainly indicate all the fundamental processes that can occur — the elementary processes from which all other processes are composed. This would be the ultimate realization of **reductionism**, the view that every phenomenon can be reduced to some more elementary set of phenomena, all the way back to a set of truly fundamental entities and interactions.

Being rather more negative, a fundamental theory of everything might not really tell us very much at all. It is hard to believe, for example, that even a supremely intelligent scientist equipped with as much computing power as he or she could desire could set to work from the theory of everything and predict the existence of the Earth, let alone something like my choice of breakfast today. They might show that the existence of an Earth-like planet, or an egg-like breakfast was *consistent* with the theory of everything, but that's a long way from predicting particular cases. There are several reasons why a theory of everything will probably not really be a theory of all that much. Here are some:

- *The problem of initial conditions.* In a fully deterministic theory, such as Newtonian mechanics, the present is determined by the past. To predict particular eventualities in the present Universe we would therefore need to know the initial state of our Universe. It may not be impossible to determine these cosmic initial conditions, but it's not clear, and it is hard to believe we will ever know for sure.

- *The problem of indeterminacy.* We have seen that when it comes to predicting particular events quantum physics is limited to making probabilistic predictions. It seems certain that quantum physics will be an underlying principle of any conceivable theory of everything, so the predictions may always be limited to possibilities rather than particular eventualities. Some might hope, as Einstein did, that quantum physics will eventually be shown to be incomplete and that a full theory will replace probability by certainty, but all current indications are that this is not going to be the case and the one thing that's certain is that uncertainty is here to stay.

- *The problem of emergence.* Reductionism was originally a biological doctrine which aimed to reduce biology to more fundamental sciences such as chemistry and physics. It was opposed by the doctrine of **emergence** which claimed that even if all physical and chemical phenomena were known it would not be possible to predict biological phenomena because new properties emerged at the level of biology that were not contained in any of its parts. These doctrines are now used generally in discussions of science, including physics. To give a physical example; water is wet and it is made of molecules, yet no molecule is wet; the wetness is a property of the water that emerges when large numbers of molecules come together. Most physicists would expect a satisfactory explanation of the wetness of water to make contact with fundamental principles (somehow, the wetness of water must be implicit in the electrical interactions of its molecules) and, in this sense, they are reductionists. But it often happens that complex phenomena require explanations on many different levels, and it would be wrong to dismiss the higher levels as being unimportant, or uninteresting to the physicist. The interactions of atoms and molecules are now understood — at least in terms of the fundamental laws that operate. Yet a wealth of unexpected phenomena continues to emerge in the physics of atoms, molecules, solids and liquids, showing that there is much to explore in physics above the most fundamental level. The challenges are as much to do with understanding the consequences of known laws as with discovering new ones. Perhaps the ultimate challenge will be to provide a chain of understanding that links fundamental principles to truly complex phenomena, such as how a brain works.

For all of these reasons, and others you can discover for yourself, it seems safe to conclude that physics has a healthy future that might well include a theory of everything, but which is very unlikely to be ended by such a theory.

6   Closing items

6.1   Chapter summary

1   Laws summarize regularities observed in Nature. They can summarize large numbers of similar phenomena and make it possible to predict the course of particular phenomena.

2   In physics, many of the laws are expressed mathematically and concern measurable quantities. This aids precision and clarity, and it supports rational argument.

3   Newtonian mechanics is based on equations (Newton's laws of motion, Newton's law of universal gravitation) that are deterministic: they have the property that the present is entirely determined by the past. Complete knowledge of the state of the Universe at any one time would make possible, in principle, the determination of its state at all other times.

4   Thermodynamics, with its emphasis on energy conservation (the first law) and entropy growth (the second law) indicates an effectively unavoidable irreversibility in the laws of Nature.

5   Electromagnetism was ultimately responsible for the introduction of the field as a new fundamental ingredient in physical world-views. Although attempts were made to formulate mechanical models of the electromagnetic field, such efforts are no longer a serious topic of scientific investigation. Fields are introduced to avoid the use of action at a distance.

6   Special relativity is based on the idea that observers in uniform motion should agree about the laws of physics. It has the effect of unifying space and time into a space-time that different observers slice into space and time in ways that depend on their relative motion.

7   General relativity represents gravity as a manifestation of space-time curvature: 'matter tells space how to curve, space tells matter how to move'.

8   Quantum physics is characterized by the intrinsic and unavoidable use of probability (implying indeterminacy in the behaviour of individual systems). Quantum mechanics is a major subdivision of quantum physics that deals with particles and calls into question the simplest kind of realism. Quantum field theory is another major subdivision of quantum physics. It deals with fields and represents a natural fusion of quantum physics and special relativity. Quantum fields can be interpreted in terms of particles and provide a good way of describing at least three of the four fundamental forces of Nature.

6.2   Achievements

Now that you have completed this chapter, you should be able to:

A1   Explain the meaning of all the newly defined (emboldened) terms introduced in this chapter.

A2   Explain what is meant by a physical world-view and describe some of the major world-views that have emerged during the evolution of physics.

A3   Describe some of the major concepts of physics, give brief biographical sketches of some of the major contributors to the development of physics and name some of the major events that have helped to shape the subject.

A4   Comment on some of the philosophical issues that are raised by the study of physics.

After using the multimedia package, you should also be able to:

A5   Install and run the multimedia package, and carry out the actions required by it.

6.3 End-of-chapter questions

Question 1.8   Express the following numbers using scientific (powers of ten) notation: (a) 2.1 million, (b) 36 000, (c) 1/10, (d) 0.000 05.

Question 1.9   List the major revolutions in physics that have occurred since 1650. Describe each in one or two sentences, giving only enough detail to distinguish it from the others.

Question 1.10   Describe the concept of a field. Briefly outline the history of this concept from the time of Faraday to the present day.

Question 1.11   Briefly describe the opposition that exists between reductionism and emergence.

Question 1.12   On the basis of dates of birth and death alone, which of the following pairs of physicists might have been able to meet for a discussion about their scientific discoveries?

(a) Galileo and Newton

(b) Newton and Laplace

(c) Laplace and Coulomb

(d) Coulomb and Faraday

(e) Faraday and Maxwell

(f) Maxwell and Einstein

(g) Einstein and Bohr

(h) Bohr and Heisenberg

(i) Heisenberg and Dirac ■

Appendix: Some highlights of physics

c. 624 BC Birth of Thales of Miletus; traditionally 'the first physicist'.

384 BC Birth of Aristotle; author of *Physics*.

1543 Nicolaus Copernicus' *De Revolutionibus Orbium Celestium*.

1600 William Gilbert's *De Magnete* describing the behaviour of magnets.

1609 Johannes Kepler's first and second laws published in *Astronomia Nova*.

1632 Galileo's *Dialogue Concerning the Two Chief Systems of the World* published.

1638 Galileo's work on motion described in his *Discorsi*.

1687 Newton's laws of motion and gravitation published in his *Principia*.

1704 Newton's work on light and spectra described in his *Opticks*.

1729 Stephen Gray discovers electrical conduction.

1736 Leonhard Euler introduces differential equations into mechanics.

1755 Euler lays the foundations of fluid mechanics.

1784 Pierre Laplace introduces concept of electric potential.

1785 Charles Coulomb announces his law of electrostatics.

1799 Pierre Laplace's *Méchanique Céleste* (Volume 1).

1801 Thomas Young demonstrates the wave nature of light.

1803 John Dalton proposes his atomic theory of matter.

1820 Hans Oersted demonstrates electromagnetism.

1821 Michael Faraday demonstrates the principle of the electric motor.

1825 Sadi Carnot lays the foundations of thermodynamics.

1843 James Joule determines the mechanical equivalent of heat.

1847 Hermann von Helmholtz formulates conservation of energy.

1848 Lord Kelvin proposes the absolute temperature scale.

1849 Armand Fizeau makes first accurate measurement of the speed of light.

1850 Rudolf Clausius introduces entropy.

1859 James Clerk Maxwell develops the kinetic theory of gases.

1865 Maxwell's *Dynamical Theory of the Electromagnetic Field*.

1871 Dmitry Mendeleev's periodic table of the elements.

1877 Ludwig Boltzmann introduces statistical interpretation of entropy.

1882 Albert Michelson measures the speed of light.

1887 Michelson–Morley experiment fails to detect the ether.

1887 Heinrich Hertz discovers photoelectric effect.

1888 Heinrich Hertz demonstrates the existence of radio waves.

1895 Wilhelm Röntgen discovers X-rays.

1896 Henri Becquerel discovers radioactivity.

1897 J. J. Thomson discovers the electron.

1900	Max Planck introduces the quantum.
1905	Einstein publishes papers on special relativity, Brownian motion and the photoelectric effect.
1911	Ernest Rutherford announces discovery of the atomic nucleus.
1911	Victor Hess discovers cosmic rays.
1913	Niels Bohr's quantum theory of the atom.
1916	Einstein's general theory of relativity.
1924	Bose–Einstein statistics introduced.
1925	Heisenberg introduces quantum mechanics (matrix form).
1925	Wolfgang Pauli announces the exclusion principle.
1926	Schrödinger introduces wave mechanics.
1926	Born's probability interpretation of quantum mechanics.
1926	Fermi–Dirac statistics introduced.
1927	Heisenberg formulates the uncertainty principle.
1928	The Dirac equation describes relativistic electrons and leads to an understanding of spin and the prediction of antiparticles.
1929	Edwin Hubble discovers the expansion of the Universe.
1932	James Chadwick discovers the neutron.
1932	Carl Anderson discovers the positron.
1934	Fermi introduces the weak interaction.
1935	Hideki Yukawa lays the foundation of the strong interaction.
1939	Otto Hahn and Lise Meitner discover nuclear fission.
1948	John Bardeen, William Brattain and William Shockley produce the transistor.
1948	Feynman introduces his diagrams for quantum electrodynamics.
1948	George Gamow proposes the basis of Big Bang theory.
1964	Murray Gell-Mann introduces quarks.
1965	Arno Penzias and Robert Wilson discover cosmic microwave background radiation.
1967	Jocelyn Bell Burnell discovers first pulsar (a neutron star).
1968	Steven Weinberg, Abdus Salam and Sheldon Glashow develop unified theory of electroweak interaction.
1972	Fritsch, Gell-Mann and Bardeen develop quantum chromodynamics.
1977	Klaus von Klitzing discovers the quantum Hall effect.
1980	Alan Guth proposes an inflationary early Universe.
1981	Green and Schwarz introduce superstring theory.
1982	Alain Aspect conducts experiment demonstrating non-local aspects of quantum physics.
1986	Bednorz and Mueller discover high-temperature superconductivity.
1991	CERN confirms the existence of three generations of fundamental particles.
1995	Witten and Townsend develop M-Theory.
1995	Cornell, Wieman and Anderson discover Bose–Einstein condensate of atomic gas.

Suggestions for further reading

If you wish to pursue some of the topics discussed in this book in greater detail you might like to start with one or other of the following works.

General

John D. Barrow (1988), *The World Within the World*, Oxford.

Richard P. Feynman (1992), *The Character of Physical Law*, Penguin Books.

Brian Greene (1999), *The Elegant Universe*, W. W. Norton.

Werner Heisenberg (1990), *Physics and Philosophy*, Penguin Books.

Jan Hilgevoord (ed.) (1994), *Physics and our view of the world*, Cambridge.

Steven Weinberg (1993), *Dreams of a final theory*, Vintage.

Historical

William Berkson (1974), *Fields of Force*, RKP.

I. Bernard Cohen (1987), *The Birth of a New Physics*, Penguin.

P. M. Harman (1982), *Energy, Force and Matter*, Cambridge.

Abraham Pais (1986), *Inward Bound*, Oxford.

Christopher Ray (1987), *The Evolution of Relativity*, Adam Hilger.

Silvan S. Schweber (1994), *QED and the men who made it*, Princeton.

Emilio Segrè (1980), *From X-rays to Quarks*, Freeman.

Emilio Segrè (1984), *From Falling Bodies to Radio Waves*, Freeman.

Biographical

On Heisenberg: D. C. Cassidy (1992), *Uncertainty*, New York.

Richard P. Feynman (1985), '*Surely You're Joking Mr. Feynman!*', Unwin.

David Gooding and Frank James (eds.) (1985), *Faraday Rediscovered*, Stockton.

Helge Kragh (1990), *Dirac*, Cambridge.

Walter Moore (1992), *Schrödinger*, Cambridge.

On Einstein: Abraham Pais (1982), *Subtle is the Lord*, Oxford.

Ivan Tolstoy (1981), *James Clerk Maxwell*, University of Chicago Press.

On Newton: Richard S. Westfall (1980), *Never at Rest*, Cambridge.

Answers and comments

Q1.1   The Chinese were perhaps right, but their complaint is more about language than substance. When we talk about a system obeying a scientific law, we do not mean that the system has understood the law and is consciously following it. We just mean that the behaviour of the system follows a pattern that is predictable, and that someone has discovered and announced this pattern as a scientific law.

Q1.2   *This question is unusually open-ended, with no single correct answer. In preparing our answer we have taken the opportunity to expand the discussion slightly, but would not expect you to include all the points listed below.*

There are several reasons why it would be impossible, in practice, to follow through the Newtonian programme of predicting the entire future of the Universe.

(i) We would need to know the positions and velocities of all the particles in the Universe at a given instant. Nowadays we know that the Universe contains an immense number of fundamental particles. The visible Universe contains about 10^{80} protons and the same number of electrons. Measuring the positions and velocities of such a large number of particles is an unimaginable task. (Indeed, there may be some regions of the Universe that are so remote that we cannot yet know of their existence because the Universe is too young for light from them to have reached us!)

(ii) In order to predict the *exact* future of the Universe, we would need to know the *exact* initial positions and velocities of all the particles. Small errors in measurement may, at first, produce only small errors in prediction, but the errors are cumulative and will eventually become serious. (Nowadays we know that some simple systems are extremely sensitive to the initial conditions. In some cases, it is impossible to measure the initial conditions accurately enough to make anything more than a very short-term prediction. Such systems are said to be *chaotic*. They will be discussed more fully in Book 3.)

(iii) We need to know all the forces acting between particles. Newton only produced an explicit formula for gravitational forces. His work was later extended to cover electromagnetic forces, but our understanding of the interactions between particles remains partial and a complete understanding elusive.

(iv) Even if we had all the information necessary, the calculations would be far too difficult to carry out. No computer could ever attempt an exact solution. And even if the calculations could be done, there would be nowhere to store all the results.

For all these reasons, we cannot hope to predict the exact future of the Universe. That would be too much to expect. The great successes of physics emerge when we ask specific questions about systems that are simple, or can be thought of as being simple, so that the mathematical analysis remains feasible for humans and their computers.

Q1.3   By the second law of thermodynamics, the total entropy of the Universe must not decrease. The entropy of warm objects placed inside the fridge decreases as heat flows from them. At the same time, the back of the fridge is warm, so the surroundings of the fridge are warmed and their entropy is increased. The second law of thermodynamics is satisfied because the increase in entropy of the surroundings of the fridge is equal or greater in magnitude than the decrease in entropy of the fridge contents.

Q1.4   Electromagnetic waves are predicted by Maxwell's equations, as disturbances of Faraday's electric and magnetic fields. The disturbances travel at the speed of light, which is finite. Thus Faraday's idea that disturbances of fields should travel at a finite speed was confirmed.

Q1.5   According to special relativity, different observers disagree about how to slice space-time up into space and time. But observers are not free to make *arbitrary* choices. All observers must find that light travels at a constant speed of $c = 2.998 \times 10^8$ metres per second, and this will not be possible if an observer uses a clock that is running slower and slower, for example. The definition of time is made quite naturally in special relativity as the time ticked on a regularly running clock that travels with the observer.

Q1.6   In quantum mechanics, identical situations do not always produce identical outcomes. Nevertheless, a certain regularity remains because if an experimental arrangement has a variety of possible outcomes, each occurring with a definite probability, subsequent repetitions of the experiment will have the same outcomes occurring with the same probabilities. By repeating the experiment a large number of times we can check whether the probabilities predicted by quantum mechanics are valid. The most important characteristic of a scientific law is that it should be open to experimental tests. Quantum mechanics has introduced a new type of scientific law — one based on probability which embraces the fact that identical situations do not produce identical outcomes.

Q1.7   Quantum field theory is based on the idea of intrinsic probability, just as ordinary quantum mechanics is. It therefore raises exactly the same questions about simple realism.

Q1.8 (a) 2.1×10^6; (b) 3.6000×10^4; (c) 1.0×10^{-1}; (d) 5×10^{-5}. Each of these answers assumes a certain level of precision. For example, 2.1 million has been interpreted as 2.1 million, rather than 2.2 million, so only two digits have been retained in scientific notation; 36 000 has been interpreted as 36 000 rather than 36 001, and this greater precision is indicated by using five digits.

Q1.9 (i) Newtonian mechanics explained the motion of particles in terms of the forces acting on them. The law of gravitation illustrated how forces could be calculated, while Newton's laws of motion showed how forces influence the motion of particles.

(ii) Thermodynamics deals with processes involving energy transfers, including heat, and clarifies ideas about equilibrium and irreversibility.

(iii) Statistical mechanics interprets thermodynamics in terms of the statistical behaviour of a large number of particles.

(iv) Electromagnetism deals with electricity and magnetism. It replaced the concept of action at a distance by that of a field, and showed that electric and magnetic fields have their own dynamics, leading to the interpretation of light and radio waves as electromagnetic waves.

(v) Special relativity is based on the idea that all observers in uniform motion should agree about the laws of physics. When the laws of electromagnetism were included, this led to a revolution in our ideas of space and time, which were merged together into space-time. Different observers, in different states of uniform motion, disagree about which events are simultaneous in space-time.

(vi) General relativity grew from the desire to express physical laws in the same way for all observers, even those who were not moving uniformly. It became a theory of gravity in which the motion of bodies was determined by the curvature of space-time, caused by sources of gravitation.

(vii) Quantum mechanics describes systems of particles in the atomic domain. It asserts that the fundamental laws of physics involve probability in an intrinsic and unavoidable way, and so casts doubt on simple realism.

(viii) Quantum field theory extends the ideas of quantum mechanics and special relativity to fields. Particles are interpreted as quanta of excitation of the field and may be created or annihilated as the field becomes more or less excited.

Q1.10 A field is a physical quantity with a value at each point in space. A particle passing through a given point will experience forces that depend on the fields at that point. Thus the concept of a field replaces action at a distance.

Faraday introduced fields in the context of magnetism and electricity, and Maxwell established the reality of these fields by showing that wave-like disturbances of electric and magnetic fields can travel through space at the speed of light. He interpreted light as an electromagnetic wave and predicted the existence of longer wavelength electromagnetic waves (radio waves). Einstein's general theory of relativity is a field theory of gravitation in which the field describes the curvature of space-time.

A quantum theory of fields was developed which incorporates ideas from quantum mechanics and special relativity. Quantum electrodynamics is an example of a quantum field theory, in which the electromagnetic field is quantized and the quanta are photons. Quantum field theory also applies to ordinary matter — there are electron fields for example, with the quanta interpreted as the electrons. In quantum field theory, quanta may be created or destroyed as the field becomes more or less excited.

Q1.11 Reductionism is an attempt to interpret everything in terms of fundamental phenomena. For a physicist, this implies trying to explain everything in terms of fundamental particles and their interactions.

Emergence stresses the fact that certain phenomena arise only in complex systems, and have no direct counterpart in terms of fundamental phenomena. For example, an iron bar has a strength that is not directly related to the strength of iron atoms.

Most physicists believe that everything can be related, in principle, to fundamental phenomena. In principle, the strength of an iron bar can be explained in terms of the forces between atoms, which in turn can be explained in terms of quantum field theory. The hard-line reductionist might therefore dismiss the strength of the rod as being of minor importance, since it is a consequence of more fundamental ideas. Most physicists (and even more engineers) would disagree. Advocates of emergence delight in the fact that new phenomena, such as rigidity, emerge from more basic laws. Far from dismissing ideas such as rigidity they use them as valid concepts in their own right.

Q1.12 Laplace and Coulomb, Faraday and Maxwell, Einstein and Bohr, Bohr and Heisenberg, and Heisenberg and Dirac could have met for a discussion of their scientific views. The other pairs either did not overlap, or did not overlap sufficiently for a meaningful scientific discussion to have been possible.

Acknowledgements

Grateful acknowledgement is made to the following sources for permission to reproduce material in this book:

Front cover – Science Museum/Science & Society Picture Library;

Fig. 0.1 COBE – NASA Goddard Space Flight Center and the COBE Science Working Group; COMA cluster of galaxies – NASA & AURA/STSc1; The Spiral Galaxy M83 – Anglo-Australian Observatory, Photograph by David Malin; The Earth's Atmosphere – NASA; Landsat photo of the Wash – Science Photo Library; Whole body picture of A. Einstein – Rijksmuseum; Integrated circuit – Science Photo Library; Ring of 48 Iron atoms – Courtesy of Don Eigler, IBM Research Division; Subatomic particle tracks – CERN/Science Photo Library. *Fig. 0.2* Courtesy of Dana Berry.

Fig. 1.1 Mansell/TimeInc./Katz; *Fig 1.2* Graham Read; *Fig. 1.3a* British Library; *Fig. 1.3b* Science Museum/Science and Society Picture Library; *Fig. 1.6* Mary Evans; *Fig. 1.7* The National Trust Photographic Library/Tessa Musgrave; *Fig. 1.8* British Library; *Fig. 1.9* By permission of the Syndics of Cambridge University Library; *Fig. 1.10* Science Museum/Science & Society Picture Library; *Fig. 1.12a* J. M. Petit Publibphoto Diffusion Science Photo Library; *Fig. 1.13* Science Museum/ Science & Society Picture Library; *Fig. 1.15* Every effort has been made to trace the copyright holder. The publisher will be pleased to make the necessary arrangements at the first opportunity; *Fig. 1.17*, *Fig. 1.18*, *Fig. 1.19*, *Fig. 1.21*, all Science Museum/Science & Society Picture Library; *Fig 1.24* Brian Steadman; *Fig. 1.25* Hulton Getty; *Fig. 1.26* The British Museum; *Fig. 1.27* By permission of Times Newspapers Limited, Copyright Times Newspapers Limited, 1919; *Fig. 1.31* Portrait by Michael Noakes, St John's College Cambridge; *Fig. 1.32a* Lawrence Berkeley Laboratory/Science Photo Library; *Fig. 1.32b* CERN; *Fig. 1.34* Courtesy of the Archives California Institute of Technology.

Index

Entries and page numbers in **bold type** refer to key words which are printed in **bold** in the text and which are defined in the Glossary. These are terms which we expect you to be able to explain the meaning of, and use correctly, both during and at the end of the course.

start ~~-right hand click~~ → left hand

run → browse →

select dish S207→

install → open→okay

or

start →right clich – explore →

dish S207 → install → welcome →

next etc.